PRACTICAL
CARRIAGE AND
WAGON PAINTING

PRACTICAL
CARRIAGE AND WAGON
PAINTING

A TREATISE ON THE PAINTING OF

CARRIAGES, WAGONS AND SLEIGHS

EMBRACING FULL AND EXPLICIT DIRECTIONS
FOR EXECUTING ALL CLASSES OF
WORK, INCLUDING

PAINTING FACTORY WORK, LETTERING, SCROLLING, ORNAMENTING, VARNISHING, ETC.

WITH MANY TESTED RECIPES AND FORMULAS

by M.C. HILLICK

WITH AN INTRODUCTION BY
MERRI FERRELL
CURATOR, CARRIAGE COLLECTION,
THE MUSEUMS AT STONY BROOK

THE ASTRAGAL PRESS
Mendham, New Jersey

Library of Congress Catalog Card Number: 97-70455
International Standard Book Number: 1-879335-77-8

PRINTED IN THE UNITED STATES OF AMERICA

Published by
THE ASTRAGAL PRESS
5 Cold Hill Road / Suite #12
Mendham NJ 07945-0239

INTRODUCTION

Horse-drawn vehicles were not merely forms of transportation or recreation. They were immensely complex artifacts that reflected not only a particular industrial and social history, but also the general aesthetic of the people who decorated and used them. The height of the "carriage era," the period in history when carriage manufacture was at its peak, was a time of eclectic and varied ornamentation decorating every conceivable object. Simultaneously there were great advances in paint and varnish manufacture, large industries unto themselves. The result was a broader palette of more durable colors to cover everything from the child's push-cart to a large omnibus.

Prospective carriage painters entered the trade as apprentices, becoming familiar with the materials through the repetition of rigorous tasks. Additional instruction was available through technical schools and the proliferation of instructive manuals and periodicals that were published for the industry. Among those publications was M.C. Hillick's *Practical Carriage and Wagon Painting*, published in 1900. The chapters of the book are organized not unlike the structure of an apprenticeship, beginning with the organization of the shop and understanding of tools, especially the various types of brushes used for different purposes, to the tedious but necessary preparation of the surface. Hillick's insightful advice is as useful today as it was at the beginning of the twentieth century. He speaks of the difficulties associated with using varnish and how to avoid typical problems such as runs, flaking, and blooming. His guide to the procedures for laying on colors shows his high degree of familiarity with his art. He includes chapters on striping business wagons and sleighs, perhaps the most highly decorated of all vehicle types.

Carriage painting was a specialized skill that served the dual purpose of providing a protective coating for the wood and metal components of a vehicle and of unifying or emphasizing various parts and materials to give the vehicle its general appearance. In summarizing the purpose of carriage painting, M.C. Hillick wrote, "Its chief attainments are, firstly, to preserve the structural parts of the vehicle from the action of the elements; secondly, from the remorseless and gnawing tooth of service; thirdly, to aid in making the vehicle really beautiful, a work of art." Ranging from simple color application and striping to complete pictorial programs, carriage painting was an integral part of the larger system of carriage manufacturing, for it was the paint that defined the character of the vehicle, that enhanced good workmanship or subdued minor flaws, that provided the images and fancy lettering to promote the wares of a commercial wagon or gave a fanciful decorated sleigh a brightness and gaiety.

The beautiful and delicate illustrations of ornaments that complement Hillick's instructive text make this an important book for any individual interested in the history of horse-drawn vehicles. It is one of the best sources for everything from the naming of striping styles to deciding which brush should be used to achieve a specific line. This book helps to illustrate that the decorations, decals, and designs that covered horse-drawn vehicles of every description were not arbitrary, but well-conceived and skillfully applied. For any afficionado of 19th or early 20th century material culture, Hillick's book offers a unique and intimate insight into the aesthetics of the time, which combined the practical with the beautiful. For graphic artists, there are scrolls, border, corner pieces, acanthus leaves and imaginative lettering. For conservators and museum professionals, this is an impressive document of materials and procedures of fabrication. *Practical Carriage and Wagon Painting* is a superbly interesting book that is as delightful as it is instructive.

Merri McIntyre Ferrell
Curator, Carriage Collection
The Museums at Stony Brook
Stony Brook, Long Island, New York

PREFACE.

It has been almost twenty years since a volume on carriage and wagon painting made its appearance in this country, during which time the enterprising carriage painter has been wide awake. He has found many new processes and a multitude of new materials of which the workman of twenty years ago knew nothing; he has raised vehicle painting from a simple mechanical process, which was intended to preserve the surface from decay, to a fine art of the highest order, and fashionable people now take as much pride in having beautiful and stylish equipages as they do in wearing clothing that is up to date, or in securing jewels that are sufficiently brilliant to dazzle all beholders.

No one realized more fully than the writer that an up-to-date work on the difficult but noble calling of the carriage and wagon painter was badly needed, so he began to cast about for someone who was fully qualified for the task of writing such a book. He knew that the author of such a work should be a man of extended trade practice and one who could divest himself of high-flown scientific terms and make his language so plain that any workman who cared to do so could easily comprehend the instruction given. A careful survey of the field led to the selection of Mr. M. C. Hillick, whose work for the magazines during the past ten or twelve years has done so much to assist carriage and wagon painters to elevate their calling to its present high standard. Mr. Hillick has long held a high place among the best-known carriage painters in this country, is thoroughly posted on all the various branches of the business, and has the happy faculty of being able to impart his knowledge to others in such a plain, practical way that they cannot fail to understand him. His excessive modesty came very near causing him to decline, but he was finally induced to undertake the work, and PRACTICAL CARRIAGE AND WAGON PAINTING is presented to a generous public with the knowledge that its superior has never made its appearance in this country.

It is but a short time since the demands of the times gave birth to that great institution—the factory shop—that monster establishment from which hundreds of vehicles are turned out daily. The writer pleads guilty to a strong prejudice against the class of work done in these factories, yet he is compelled to admire the finished product and applaud the genius of the painter who can thus marshal his forces and, by working to a set of fixed rules, seem to defy natural laws, and out of it all bring a thing of beauty which, while it does not prove a "joy forever," does possess a degree of durability that we of the old school of carriage painters were led to believe was impossible. It has remained for Mr. Hillick to take us through this great establishment, and he describes the processes and gives us the formulas that are employed, in such plain, helpful language that no one can read his words without profit as well as pleasure.

Time and space forbid (even if I had the ability to give it) a comprehensive review of this work. It would be impossible to enumerate the millions of good points it possesses, so it is best to let the succeeding pages speak for themselves. They will do it much more eloquently than I could hope to do. I am sure of one fact, and it is that if carriage and wagon painters all over the world will read and practice the teachings of the succeeding chapters they will become better painters, better citizens, and our country roads, as well as our boulevards, will sparkle with a stream of better painted and more beautiful vehicles.

When the writing of PRACTICAL CARRIAGE AND WAGON PAINTING was committed to Mr. Hillick, the writer expected great things of him. Now, as I look over the chapters of the completed work, I am happily conscious of the fact that I am not disappointed in the slightest degree, and I wish to thank Mr. Hillick for giving to the vehicle world a work on painting that will prove helpful to the master workman as well as to the ambitious apprentice.   CHAS H. WEBB.

Chicago, April, 1898.

CONTENTS.

INTRODUCTORY.

I
N many of its elementary principles the art of carriage and wagon painting as at present exemplified does not materially differ from the art as it
was interpreted in the remote past. Processes and systems have
changed and adapted themselves to the swifter modes of life, but not a few
of the paint materials, especially those used in the foundation and surfacing
coats, remain practically the same as used in former times. The P. W. F.'s,
as surfacing agents expected to take the place of white lead and oil and their
assistant pigments, tossed merrily upon the topmost wave of favor for a
brief period some two decades ago, but the fiat of their decline went forth
and at the present time the great majority of carriage and wagon painters
still adhere to white lead, raw linseed oil, ochres, and regulation roughstuff
pigments for their foundation materials, as did their instructors and
predecessors.

The abbreviated time allowance accorded the painter for the painting
and finishing of a vehicle has made necessary a readjustment of proportions
of both liquid and pigment ingredients which, it must be confessed, has
operated in a way harmful to the natural durability of the material employed.
The painter, however, can in no wise be held responsible for the general
lack of durability which is said to distinguish the painting of the present as
compared to that of the past. The great inexorable Public is the master,
the painter its unwilling but submissive servant.

Nevertheless, conditions of permanency and durability are still wrought
and achieved in the modern field of carriage and wagon painting, conditions
which conform, with a large measure of credit to the art of painting, to the
other resultant durable effects obtained along nearly all other lines of
industrial activity.

Our painting today fails to excel the painting of tradition simply
because the exactions of a wonderfully fast age tend directly to promote
failure rather than to aid success.

The job of painting which withstands fierce and continuous attacks of
service for a reasonable length of time must be justly registered durable,
regardless of what it would have been termed in the past. Past conditions
and circumstances cannot fairly be used as yardsticks to measure what we
at present call beautiful and enduring in the art of painting.

In the matter of tools, appliances for handling work, colors and
varnishes used, carriage and wagon painting, amid the advances made in all
the other constructive departments of industry, has enjoyed improvement.
Brushes in greater variety, finer in quality, and better adapted to the

practical needs of the painter, are in evidence. Colors of a wider range of hues, tints, shades, and incomparably finer as to quality than were obtainable formerly, are now at the disposal of the painter. And the varnishes—surely they have been improved, made more reliable, more uniform in quality, better behaved and more suited to the ever-varying requirements of service.

Carriage and wagon painting has become as much of a business as an artistic venture. Commercial conditions have of late years so shaped themselves that the painter, to successfully conduct a painting business, must of necessity study the profound science of business quite as thoroughly as he does the science of building paint structures and developing color effects. He imparts a moral, business, and mechanical force to the community. He now has available sources of education more easily within his reach than at any former time. Paint trade literature, so far as it is represented in magazine form at least, is at hand to render him aid and encouragement. He is rapidly becoming better fitted to meet the expanding limits of competition, to critically analyze both the theory and practice of painting, to become, in short, a greater power for good in the community as well as a studious and original mechanic.

In the inseparable community of business interests, the painting of the vehicular equipment has reached the level of a prominent industry.

Its chief attainments are, firstly, to preserve the structural parts of the vehicle from the action of the elements; secondly, from the remorseless and gnawing tooth of service; thirdly, to aid in making the vehicle really beautiful, a work of art.

The mission of the following chapters will be to record the systems, methods, and processes practiced in modern carriage and wagon painting, to the end that the apprentice—good luck to him, and may he pluck the peach from the sunniest side of the fence always—may be enlightened, that the already skilled workman may be interested somewhat, and that the trade of carriage and wagon painting may be welcomed as a delightful guest, worthy of enthusiastic entertainment.

CHAPTER I.

THE SHOP AND ITS EQUIPMENT.

"Give ample room and verge enough."—Gray.

IT would not be fit nor seemly to lay down any arbitrary rules for the guidance of the painter in the selection or construction of the paint shop. Conditions and circumstances here control. But so far as the painter is able to have authority in the matter it should be directed in favor of large, roomy apartments, high ceilings, and a fine outfit of windows. Light is an indispensable commodity in the paint shop. And room—there is never an excess of it. To do good work at a profit invokes an easy, commodious working space. To this end, therefore, the painter may well direct his best endeavors. Nor should the ventilation be neglected. A ventilator in quite common use, old-time but effective when the construction of the shop permits of its use, consists of the regulation stove pipe, say 12 inches in diameter and extending 18 inches or 2 feet above the roof of the building, furnished at its upper extremity with a revolving hood or cap. The local tinsmith usually has an invention of his own in the way of revolving ventilators which is workable and nicely suited to the needs of the paint shop. Where ceiling ventilators are not practicable, apertures some 8 inches in diameter may be made in the walls well up toward the ceiling, one or two on each side of the room, according to the size and location, and into these apertures insert tin frames, both ends of which are covered with wire gauze, the gauze on the inside or room end of the fixture being fitted to a hinged lid frame. Into this tin and gauze compartment put clean curled hair or moss. Metal caps may be fitted to cover the inside opening of these ventilators, so that if necessary the air can be shut out entirely so far as entrance through these channels is

FIG. 1—WHEEL JACK.

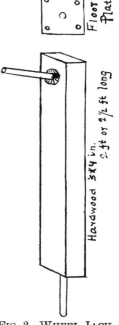

FIG. 2—WHEEL JACK.

concerned.   There are numerous other styles of ventilators, but they do not call for mention, as local and individual needs will suggest the kind most feasible to adopt.

The mixing bench should be located in a light corner of the room.   It should be furnished with a slab of marble or stone, preferably marble.   A cupboard with tightly fitting doors should be over, or at the side of, the bench with specially p r e p a r e d b o a r d s on which to wipe brushes near at hand.   A first-class paint mill should be a fixture in close proximity to the paint bench.

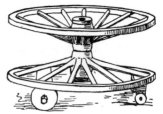

FIG. 4—LONG-ACRE BODY TRESTLE.

The varnish room (sacred temple of the painter's hopes shall we say?), over which men rarely fail to disagree, needs to be every inch as

FIG. 3.

large as conditions will permit.   It should have ventilators, such as above described or similar, in plenty.   The gauze and tin funnel ventilators might well be used near the floor and ceiling, thus driving the room impurities up and out.   The varnish room cannot well be too large, nor too light, nor too cosy.   Nor can it follow too closely the Quaker's code as to furnishings, for "unadorned, adorned the most" strictly applies to this historic apartment.

FIG. 5—BODY TRESTLE.   FIG. 6—BODY AND GEAR TRESTLE.

It is agreed that the northeast corner of the shop is the best location for the varnish room.   The north light is the most restful and the easiest light to work by, and it is esteemed the best drying light.   The room ought not to be placed immediately over the smith shop.   It should have plenty of windows, north and east, and made to lower at the top.   If possible, have a hardwood floor, and oiled, with ceiling and side walls of matched lumber, good quality and preferably painted white or some very light color, that it will reflect the light. Personally, I am in favor of blue colored shades for north windows and yellow ones for east and west windows. If possible, connect a "set room," provided with abundance of light, with the varnish room, into which the work may be removed the morning after finishing. The varnish room requires a small cupboard for holding varnish, cups, dusters, brushes, chamois skins, sponges, etc., a body trestle or two, a few

FIG. 7—GEAR FRAME.

FIG. 8—SEAT FRAME.

wooden, low-cut horses for supporting the varnished work, a stove, if the shop be not heated by other means, a sliding door or two, and—that's all.

The colors, pigments, and brushes will be considered in their appropriate order as the chapters proceed. Many shop fixtures will be similarly presented.

The work-handling appliances here furnished have been observed, studied, and many of them used by the writer in his travels up and down the land of paint shops. The revolving wheel jack is an indispensable fixture in the paint shop. Fig. 1 has a plank base, and an axle for a

FIG. 9—FRAME FOR BODIES.

FIG. 10—GEAR HORSE.

standard. The cut shows how it is made. Many shops use it. Fig. 2 is frequently seen in provincial paint shops. It consists of a hardwood scantling of the size noted in the cut, with a ⅝-inch or ¾-inch round iron stuck into one end and projecting 7 inches out. A hole to nicely take the iron is bored through the floor into a joist, a floor plate is placed over it, and the upright is ready to revolve. A tapering piece of round iron ¾ inch at the base is driven through the upper end of the standard, having a projection of 7 or 8 inches. A thick metal washer is then slipped over the arm, thus completing the fixture.   Fig. 3 is largely used in factory shops.   It is the finest wheel jack extant.   Observe the bottom.   Almost any foundry will cast one at from $1.25 to $1.50 each.   Weight, from 40 to 60 lbs.; diameter, 18 to 20 inches; hole for insertion of arm, 1 inch to 1¼ inches.   Weld stub axle to the round arm.   Have varying sizes of axle stubs, from ¾, ⅞, and 1 inch to 1¼ inches.   This is a particularly fine jack for wheel striping purposes.   Can be easily transferred to any part of the shop, and runs true.

The Long-Acre body trestle, a London production, is often met with in the paint shop.   Fig. 4 shows it in working order, on rollers, and the wheels connected with a wooden pin for a pivot.   Fig. 5 is a second body trestle, neat, easy to work, and the cut quite completely explains how it is built.   Height, and proportion of parts can be made to suit the individual fancy.   Fig. 6 represents a combination body and gear trestle largely used

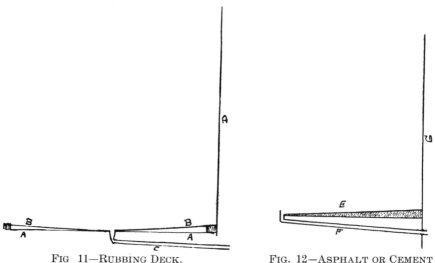

FIG 11—RUBBING DECK.   FIG. 12—ASPHALT OR CEMENT
                                              DECK.

in factory paint shops.   Height, 3 ft., 2 in.; length of revolving frame pieces, 27 in., 2x2 in. in size.   A 4x4-inch piece 9 in. long supports the frame. Inclined pieces are 25 in. long; size, 2x2 in.   The trestle is of hardwood, or should be, bolted together.   Fig. 7, a gear frame, fits onto the frame of Fig. 6.   It should be 4 ft., 6 in. long and 14 in. wide.   It easily takes the shortest gears as well as the longest, and the workman is enabled to always obtain the best possible light.   Fig. 8 is a seat frame made to fit the trestle, Fig. 6.   Make it of 1-inch stuff.   Length, 2 ft.; height at rear, 9 in.; front, 2 in.; width, 13½ in., to fit frame.   This holds a carriage seat in capital shape for painting and finishing.   Fig. 9 is a frame for holding bodies while varnishing them or while rubbing the varnish.   One-inch pine boards 6 in. in width afford good material for the frame.   Let it be from 32 to 36 in. high, about the same in length, and 27 in. wide.   At top of standards bolt

7x1-inch pieces 6 in. long, containing steel brads to hold the work in place. Fig. 10 is a horse for holding carriage gears during the process of painting and finishing. Gear horses can't all be revolving ones, and this one is strong and handy to work around. Make the legs of 3x1½ pine or ash and the bed piece, to which the iron standards are bolted, of ash 3x3 inches. Bolt the legs to the bed piece and stay them in the middle. The iron standards, ⁵⁄₁₆ in. thick and 1½ in. wide, are cranked over at right angles, as shown in cut, bolted firmly to bed piece, and at upper ends are hollowed out to hold the axle arms. Height of horse, 30 to 34 inches; width, wide enough to take a gear from 4 ft. to 5 ft., 4 in. Let the iron standards go 30 inches long, cranked at the middle. A rubbing deck for roughstuff and varnish rubbing, washing up work, etc., is a necessity even in the small shop. Fig. 11 explains an inexpensive one. A A is the shop floor, D the wall, B B the false or double floor inclining to the center, where a shallow metal gutter is let into the floor opening to a waste pipe which conveys all the waste matter outside the shop. The outer edges of the double floor rest upon stoutly-secured blocks of wood. Fig. 12 shows an asphalt or cement rubbing deck in general use in many leading shops. G is the shop wall, F the waste pipe, E the deck. The asphalt deck is not an expensive fixture, neither wears nor rusts out, and, like Fig. 11, is a practical time saver. And along with the rubbing deck the

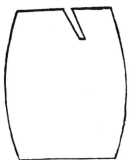

FIG. 13—DECK BARREL.

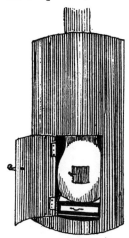

FIG. 14—VARNISH ROOM STOVE.

painter should adopt measures for securing a plentiful supply of clean soft water for shop uses, and, if possible, have it piped directly to the rubbing deck. These are days of hard-fought business battles, and any aid that will out-foot one's competitor is an effective aid. A good water supply right at hand helps mightily. Fig. 13 is a deck barrel for holding a ready supply of water for the rubber; also for holding certain styles of carriage and cutter bodies while rubbing. The slit cut at an angle lets a buggy, surrey, or other carriage seat in, and holds it fast while the rubbing proceeds.

The varnish room stove, when one is forced to use such a fixture, gives the painter much concern. In Fig. 14 is to be observed a way of enclosing the stove in sheet-iron, after the fashion of the railroads once upon a time. Cut an opening in the wall separating the varnish room from some one of the other apartments, set the stove just inside the varnish room, inclose it in the sheet-iron cylinder, making the cylinder fit close into the wall opening, and have the opening to the stove, and the stove door, reached from the room adjoining the varnish room.   Even when wholly located in the varnish room such a cylinder, enclosing the stove all over, is a practical reducer of stove dirt, etc.

NOTE.—Figs. 3, 5, 6, and 14 of this chapter, and Figs. 1, 2, and 3 of Chaptèr II. are published by permission of the *Hub.*

CHAPTER II.

BUYING AND SELECTING BRUSHES—CARE OF THEM—SOFTENING HARD BRUSHES—BRUSH KEEPERS—PRESERVING LIQUIDS—BRUSHES USED IN VEHICLE PAINTING, ETC.

ONE conspicuously famous brush maker has declared the art of brush making to be "an art preservative." The carriage and wagon painter is deeply concerned in the achievements of that art, because every distinct advancement made therein makes possible an equally distinct advancement in the art of painting. To a greater extent, perhaps, than any other class of painters, the carriage and wagon painter should be interested in making up his brush equipment of tools of the best quality. The brush made of reliable stock, having the proper "hang" and point, and which balances like a "thoroughbred," is an economical tool to buy, regardless of the price. The vehicle painter requires a brush made scientifically, by the outlay of honest workmanship, and of material that is wholly above suspicion. A brush that has simply the price to recommend it is usually an unreliable article and worketh evil, like a thief in the night, unexpectedly. In making choice of a brush for putting on priming, lead, and roughstuff, and for such other features of general use as require a round or oval bristle brush, the painter may properly look at the filling of the tool. Deception, if practiced at all, is usually placed where it shows the least. The first-class brush is distinctively the brush that shows good quality—uniform quality—

Fig. 1.

from center to outside. Other things being equal, the brush that is made up uniformly as to its bristle equipment will develop a good point, and all carriage painters are alive to the importance of this virtue in both paint and varnish brushes.

Much of the usefulness of a brush depends upon the manner of caring for it when it comes into the paint shop. The bristle brushes used for priming, lead, and roughstuff require bridling until worn down somewhat. There are many patent brush bridles now procurable at a nominal cost which tend to give a brush much better shape than the shop-made bridle. If these are not at hand, the painter can take "tufting cord" (our friends, the carriage trimmers, keep it) and wind the brush securely but not too tightly; or he can take a piece of light weight rubber cloth and, extending the piece well down on the handle, tie it at the

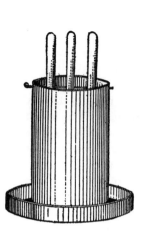
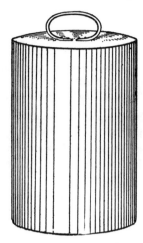

FIG. 2.

proper distance around the bristles. The rubber side of the piece should be fastened next the bristles. Then, from where it is tied around the bristles, fold the piece back onto the handle and tie securely. Trim off, and a bridle is furnished that is perfectly water-and paint-proof, the cloth side of the rubber being folded inside. For a shop-made bridle the writer finds this a serviceable one. After bridling, drop a little oil paint into the heel of the brush and set it away in a dustproof compartment for a few days. Then use the brush for a time in oil paint, suspending the brush when not in use

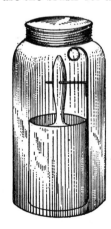

FIG. 3.

in raw linseed oil. In the course of two or three days the brush may be put into other paint if desired and suspended in water. Suspend the brush just up to the butts of the bristles, or so they are just covered, and invariably keep the water up to that point. Under no circumstances permit a brush to rest upon its point when not in use. It destroys the form of the tool and lessens its spring and elasticity. The bristle paint brushes require a clean storage quite to the extent that the color or varnish brushes do. Therefore, the receptacle in which they are kept should be fitted with a cover and should be tight enough to keep out all forms of dirt. A common tobacco pail procured of the local grocery, painted inside and out, fitted with a cover, and having nails driven at certain

COMPLETE SET OF FINISHING (FLOWING) BRUSHES.

CAMEL-HAIR FLOWING BRUSH.

COACH DUSTER.

distances apart all around it, one-third of the way down from the top, on which the brushes may be suspended, makes a cheap and excellent keeper for the ordinary paint brushes.

CHISELED PAINT BRUSH.

Camel's hair color brushes may well have a little paint, one-half oil and one-half turpentine, dropped into the heels of them. These brushes, used in japan ground colors, need to be kept suspended in water. Change the water frequently and make sure that it is clean. A brush keeper such as is recommended for varnish brushes is one of the best possible keepers for color brushes. It insures cleanliness. And vehicle painting without cleanliness is like unto a landscape painting with the beauties of nature left out. The brushes kept in water do better in rain water than in hard water. During the cold months, especially in shops where freezing is liable to occur, it is advisable to add a little glycerine to the water. The glycerine delays the freezing point and does not injure the brushes. Never soak a brush in water before using it in paint. Animal fat circulates in the capillary tubes of all bristles and hair, and if water is soaked into these arteries, the spring and elasticity of the brush is not only destroyed, but it speedily becomes a very much water-logged tool. To swell up a brush which for some cause has become dried out and shrunken, part the bristles so that the end of the handle is exposed, and pour in a small quantity of water, say three or four teaspoonfuls. Then stand it away, bristles up, handle down, for two or three hours and the brush will have returned to its normal condition. If a brush handle gets smeared with paint or varnish, a wire scrub brush dipped in a solution of sal soda will clean off the sticky substance in short order. To test the bristles in a brush, remove some of them and submit them to a smart flame. Bristles, the real animal product, will curl and writhe and emit a peculiar odor. No known adulterant burns this way.

ROUND PAINT BRUSH.

A brush that has been allowed through accident or neglect to get "soggy" may be limbered up nicely by soaking in heated turpentine. Hardened brushes may often be softened into workable condition again by soaking the bristles in hot linseed oil. A simple soaking in turps or benzine will sometimes effect the needed softening up. Brushes, however, that have dried up, saturated with quick drying colors or paint, can at best never be

CAMEL-HAIR COL-
OR BRUSH.

OVAL CHISELED VAR-
NISH BRUSH.

BADGER-HAIR
FLOWING BRUSH.

restored to a first-class working condition.   The best form of economy, therefore, is to throw such brushes away. Remedies in impressive array have been marshalled wherewith to restore varnish brushes that have become lousy, but the vehicle finisher recognizes no reliable or economical remedy for the purpose named.   A dirty varnish brush can be cleaned by washing in oil first, then in turps, and lastly worked in for putting on first rubbing coats, and thus gradually brought back to its original cleanliness.   But the varnish brush once lousy, look you! *always* lousy.   Better

"To the fire I now consign thee,
Peace unto thine ashes be."

When a varnish brush is accidentally dropped on the floor while being used, pick it up carefully and, holding it at an acute angle, bristles down, pour a small quantity of turpentine over it, thus flooding the accumulated dirt completely off.

There is a considerable diversity of opinion as to the best preserving liquid in which to keep the varnish brushes.   Local needs and requirements are probably the safest guides in the matter of choosing preserving liquids for varnish brushes.   When the brushes are used daily, as they are in big shops, it is a very good way to keep them in raw linseed oil.   Then, every morning before beginning work, the brushes may be rinsed out in turpentine, wiped out clearly over the edge of the cup, and an elastic brush full of life is assured.

Brushes used daily upon clean surfaces are, or should be, clean, and rinsing in turpentine can do no harm to a clean brush.   But in the case of brushes used every two or three days or occasionally, different treatment is needed.   Such brushes are liable to be used upon surfaces and amid surroundings less cleanly than those which obtain in the fine factory or custom shop, and the rinsing in turps, consequent upon preserving them in oil, would merely serve to loosen and set in motion the dirt and flocculent matter gradually collected and forced up into the body of the tools.   For this reason it were better to keep them in finishing varnish or, preferably, brush keeping varnish, i. e., varnish minus its driers. Whatever the preservative, the brushes require the most watchful attention. If kept in finishing varnish, the liquid should

be changed frequently. So delicate a tool, of which so much is expected, makes imperative the observance of gentle, cleanly treatment. Varnish brushes ought never to be left lying around for any considerable length of time when not in use. Dust is never idle, but always moving and, like the dew of the evening, it falleth upon the just and the unjust, varnish brushes included. Have a stiff, partly-worn brush to clean the handles of varnish brushes. Wiping them with cloth distributes lint.

In Fig. 1 is shown a double compartment brush keeper. It can be made of tin or zinc and is not expensive. Attach lock and key to it, and the brushes conditioned to a peerless trim are secure. Make the keeper 8 in. long, 5 in. wide, 9 in. deep; outfit with spring fasteners, run wires through 3 in. from top, and ¾ in. from bottom of the can locate a rack made of small wires criss-crossed on a light wire frame. The dirt

SPOKE BRUSH.

which collects in the keeper goes to the bottom beneath the gauze rack, and should a brush fall into the preserving liquid it is held aloof from the dirt accumulations. These are regulation brush keepers, clean, durable, and cost in the neighborhood of $1. Fig. 2 represents the famous thirty-cent brush keeper, several times illustrated but still deserving a place here. It is claimed to be made upon scientific principles, namely, the break between the body of the keeper and its lid or cover occurs at the bottom and below the point of brush suspension, instead, as in the ordinary keeper, at the top and above the point of suspension. It can be made of any size to meet individual needs. Such a can affords a splendid keeper for camel's-hair color brushes and for color-and-varnish brushes. Fig. 3 displays what has been somewhat widely heralded as the western idea of a brush keeper, although the gentleman who first published a

CHISELED
FITCH TOOL.

cut of the keeper and who, I believe, was the inventor of it, has seldom, if ever, been given credit for his ingenuity. My veteran brother of the brush, Mr. V. B. Grinnell, is deserving of the thanks of the trade for his invention. It consists of an ordinary glass fruit can (a metal top with rubber attachment is best), in which is located a tin cup, having a heavy wire soldered to it and projecting up to near the top of the can. This allows the cup to be easily removed from the top of the can. A second wire is soldered onto the first one so that it projects out horizontally over the cup, allowing for the suspension of the brushes in the liquid contained in the cup. The illustration shows how the keeper is made completely. Two or three brushes may be kept in each can, and they may be kept air-tight, too, a matter of moment to the vehicle painter.

The vehicle painter's brush equipment should consist of a good assortment of round or oval bristle brushes for putting on priming, lead, and roughstuff. For the best grade of carriage painting, the chiseled brush is advised for the priming and lead coats. In size they should run about 4-0. For working upon large surfaces, however, larger brushes will be needed, hence any exact size cannot be advised to meet all cases. Spoke brushes, dusters in plenty, flat chiseled bristle paint brushes, extra thick camel's-hair color brushes, varying in size from 1 in. to 3 in., camel's-hair flowing brushes, 1½ to 2½ in. in size, for applying color-and-varnish of some kinds, chiseled badger hair brushes, double thick, 1 in. to 2

PEAR FLOW-ING VARNISH BRUSH.

in. for varnishing gears, oval chiseled sash tools for cleaning up surfaces and painting when needed certain parts of a vehicle, chiseled fitch tools for cleaning up panels, and lastly not less than four sets of varnish brushes for varnishing vehicle body surfaces, along with some oval or round chiseled varnish brushes required especially in wagon painting.

The painter needs a set of at least three brushes, 1 in., 1½ in., and 2½ in. in size, for varnishing the inside surfaces of bodies, these to be used for no other purpose. Then, properly, he should have a set of brushes for putting on first rubbing varnish coats, consisting of a 1-inch chiseled badger hair brush, and a 2½ in. and one 3-in. bristle brush. Then another set of the same number for the remaining rubbing coats.

The finishing kit of brushes may properly consist of five chiseled half elastic flowing brushes, as follows: One 1-in., one 1½-inch, one 2-in., one 2½-in., one 3-in. Some finishers prefer a 1-in. badger hair brush for flowing the edges of the panels, but the set of flowing brushes herewith illustrated answers every purpose fully and completely. The art of fine brush making has so far advanced within recent years that it is now possible to get varnish brushes which require but very little working in varnish to

LONG-HANDLED SPOKE BRUSH.

prepare them for flowing on the finishing coats.

To clean a new varnish brush preparatory

to using it as a finishing brush, first draw the stock of the tool through the fingers, continuing this operation until the loose dirt is quite fully worked out. Then repeatedly submerge it in clean linseed oil and wipe out over the edge of a cup, after which use it for a week or two in rubbing varnish. The brush may then safely be used for applying finishing coats of varnish.

All brushes not specially mentioned in the foregoing as round or oval brushes are assumed to be flat, this style of brush being the one chiefly employed in vehicle painting.

In the matter of camel's-hair, badger hair, and flowing varnish brushes, the painter desires said brushes to be tough, durable fibre, having soft ends, elastic, and which wear soft until worn out.

OVAL CHISELED SASH TOOL.

CHISELED FLOWING VARNISH BRUSH.

In selecting the brush equipment, it is a most happy mental exercise to remember that the highest type of brush, if not mightier than the sword, at least hath its victories.

The numerous accompanying excellent illustrations of brushes specially adapted to the needs of the carriage and wagon painter are the result of valuable and courteously exteneded assistance tendered by that celebrated brush making firm, John L. Whiting and Son Co., Boston, Mass.

CHAPTER III.

PRIMING—LEAD COATS—RUB LEAD—KNIFING LEAD—PUTTY AND PUTTY-
ING—SANDPAPERING—ROUGHSTUFF, APPLYING AND RUBBING IT—
MATERIALS USED IN FOUNDATION COATS—MIXING FORMULAS, ETC.

FINE and durable carriage and wagon painting cannot be accomplished upon foundations in anywise weak or unstable. The supreme aim of the painter, then, should be to begin at the base of the foundation and, with patient toil and skill, aided by materials of recognized value, bring up a surface of uniform excellence and quality.

MATERIALS.

White lead and raw linseed oil; an invincible combination in the old days—shall we not say invincible still? Assuredly, nothing surpasses it today when conditions are favorable to its proper treatment; nothing upon the horizon of coming events bids fair to surpass it. It is only when the limitations of time intervene, when we must perforce bow down and worship the great American idol, Hurry, that the sinewy strength and permanency of white lead, linseed oil, and the few other constituents which enter into the foundation coats, are seriously shattered.

White lead, for example, must of necessity figure as an elemental part of the lead coats, if not of the priming, of putty, and of roughstuff. It is not now impossible to find primers being used entirely devoid of lead, but the burden of proof remains favorable to the excellence of lead. A pigment filler is quite as necessary as a liquid one. And pure white lead, Dutch process, if it please my readers—observe its properties in this respect: It is of great density, body, permanent to a rare degree, of impalpable smoothness when properly ground, and chemically unites with oil, forming a kind of varnish, which makes it a filler and pore sealer of great value. In addition, it absorbs more oil, solidifies it, and remains elastic for a greater length of time, except red lead perhaps, than any other pigment so far discovered. Moreover, it mixes happily with all other pigments which do not contain a sulphur ingredient. Briefly, these are the properties which recommend it to the carriage painter. Its noble running mate, raw linseed oil—what of it as a paint oil? Its chief virtue lies in the fact that when exposed to the air it gradually, in drying, absorbs a large proportion of oxygen, which, it is declared by Hurst, "forms a new compound of a resinous character," remarkably elastic and stable.

Since the failure of the P. W. F.'s and various other substitutes for the historic lead and oil surfacing agents, to meet the exacting needs of the trade, the swift processes now practiced have pressed into service time quickening aids which, in a work of this kind, it would scarcely seem fit to omit.

Many painters have adopted yellow ochre as a main ingredient for priming, and in particularly hurried instances, or, in fact, in the priming of a certain grade of regular factory work, varnish and, to some extent, turpentine are used. Ochre of good quality, finely ground (a coarse ground ochre is worthless in carriage painting), and containing a strong percentage of silica, is a valuable component of priming. Silica is an acknowledged pore filler, and in many of the wood fillers heralded along the highway of commerce it is the *piece de resistance*. A high grade ochre is a good drying and a very permanent pigment. It is a first-class surfacing material and not easily affected by atmospheric or other impurities. Thus we have the ingredients which, properly combined and manipulated, form the basis of all beautiful and durable carriage painting as guaged according to present day standards. Let us now consider the separate parts of the foundation building.

PRIMING.

Priming is the agent required to go into and saturate the minute cells and pores of the wood, getting a firm grip of the fibers, sealing them against moisture, and affording the painter a tough, elastic ground for his leveling materials to follow.

Primer No. 1.—White lead and raw linseed oil, darkened to a lead color with lampblack. A teaspoonful of coach japan to be added to each pint of the mixture, or omitted, as the time limit may impose.

No. 2.—White lead, 2 parts; yellow ochre, 1 part. Liquid, raw linseed oil. The use of japan to depend upon circumstances.

No. 3.—White lead, 1 part; yellow ochre, 2 parts. Liquid, raw linseed oil.

No. 4.—White lead, 1 part; yellow ochre, 2 parts. Liquids, rubbing varnish $\frac{1}{4}$; turpentine $\frac{1}{4}$; raw linseed oil $\frac{1}{2}$. A tablespoonful of japan to each quart of the mixture. This is a very quick primer, that can be sandpapered the day following its application.

No. 5.—White lead, shaded with lampblack. Liquids, rubbing varnish 1 part; raw linseed oil 5 parts.

In the above formulas keg lead is referred to.

Priming should contain just enough pigment to stain the oil. Only in this form does it perform the functions of a primer. Some hardwood surfaces, negative in composition, require a priming thinned somewhat with turpentine; otherwise such close textured spaces of wood are not sufficiently penetrated by the oily particles of the priming. The durability of the priming rests largely upon the penetration of the oil into the arteries of the wood along with a certain necessary per cent. of the pigment.

It is a good plan not to follow the surfacing of a job in the wood shop too closely with the priming. Immoderate pressure of the wood fibres usually results from the pressure of the wood worker's leveling methods. Give the wood time to expand before priming, but not time to absorb moisture. Graining out of surfaces often results from priming a surface too soon as well as too late. Many factors must necessarily be considered in order to have the priming coat do all that it should do. The condition of the wood, the climate, season, atmosphere, etc., all require diligent study. The application of the priming to the surface deserves particular attention. Granted that first-class filling and surfacing pigments, combined with liquids rich in gummy resinous matters, make the ideal primer, the coating fails of its mission when practices of neglect mark its application to the surface.

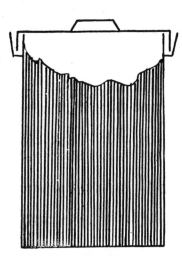

PUTTY-HOLDER.

Therefore, apply the priming smoothly and in a uniform film to the surface. Coat all parts of a job, outside, top, bottom—everywhere. Insist upon its being well brushed out—just as any coat of paint should be.

THE LEAD COATS.

What we shall be pleased to term "first lead" was formerly made of white (keg) lead thinned to a brushing consistency with linseed oil and turpentine, half and half. That was at a time when egg-shell gloss coats were in demand. A different principle has been established of late years in reference to the composition of the lead coats, and the egg-shell gloss is now regarded with suspicion and, to a large extent, abandoned altogether.

Consequently, the first lead should be mixed of $\frac{3}{8}$ oil to $\frac{5}{8}$ turps, or even with a still smaller percentage of oil if the limitations of time so direct. Apply this lead with a bristle brush and enforce rigidly the rule of smoothness and sleek brushing out.

"Second lead" means in modern paint shop lingo "flat lead"—a lead that dries to a dull, lustreless appearance, practically "dead lead." It is composed of white lead, thinned to a working consistency with turpentine, and given a binder of oil to the extent of, say $\frac{2}{3}$ of a tablespoonful of oil to a pint of the lead. These lead coats should properly contain 1 teaspoonful of japan to a pint of the lead, and be shaded with lampblack. The flat, or dead, lead is best applied with a camel's-hair brush.

RUB LEAD.

In connection with these lead coats attention must be directed to the rub lead process as a part of the system of lead surfacing now practiced in

the leading shops of the country. The rub lead is usually used directly
upon the priming coat. There are several formulas in circulation for the
mixing of the lead, but the writer thinks the one here given (used in the
leading factory paint shops) covers the painter's practical needs fully. Mix
dry white lead to a grinding consistency in ¾ raw linseed oil to ¼ japan,
the liquids to be carefully measured. Add enough lampblack to give the
mixture a clean slate color, then run through the paint mill, after which
reduce to a brushing consistency with the proper proportions of oil and
japan. Make the lead just stiff enough to brush on with a fairly stiff bristle
brush. Apply to the surface and, after permitting the mixture to take on a
"tack" for a quarter of an hour or more as the drying conditions of the
apartment may be favorable or otherwise, proceed to rub the lead into the
surface with the palm of the hand. For getting a fine, velvety, and very
dense surface of pigment, the rub lead system has no rival. However, it
cannot be worked over and re-coated so soon after being applied (it should
be given 48 hours in which to dry) as can the knifing lead. This

KNIFING LEAD,

or "glazing lead," or "draw putty," as it is variously and locally known,
renders it possible to quickly fill and level up a surface, making it compact
and solid as to texture.

Knifing lead, No. 1.—Dry white lead ⅔; keg lead ⅓. Liquids, rubbing varnish and japan, thinning to the exact working consistency with a
little turps.

No. 2.—Dry white lead, mixed in equal parts of rubbing varnish and
japan.

No. 3.—Dry white lead ⅝; keg lead ¼; roughstuff filler (finely ground)
⅛. Liquids, rubbing varnish ½; japan ¼; turpentine ¼. This last for
large panels.

These leads should all be colored slightly in the direction of the final
color to be used upon the work. Carriage and wagon painters use knifing
lead on running parts very largely, and especially upon work that must be
gotten out quicker than the rub lead would permit. On the panels of
business wagons of the medium grade, knifing lead is used to the exclusion
of roughstuff. On such panels it is advisable to apply the lead with a
bristle brush, applying the lead to the surface a little heavier in body than
ordinary paint, and then shortly going over it with a broad blade putty
knife, pressing the pigment into the wood and removing the surplus.

Knifing lead deserves to be used and applied with circumspect care and
skill if the best and most durable results would be achieved. It demands a
firm pressing into the cellular fabric of the wood, accompanied by a clean,
tidy removal of all the pigment not actually necessary to the full and
complete development of the surface. But little sandpapering should be
needed to fit it for any of the succeeding coats of material.

In the painting of running parts of the best grade, when rub lead or knifing lead is employed, the second lead, previously designated as "flat" or "dead" lead, should be employed over the rub or knifing lead, the puttying of the deep cavities and indentations being done directly upon said rub or knifing leads.

PUTTY—MAKING AND USING IT.

Putty No. 1.—The putty of history—past, present, and shall we say of

the future?—so far as history applies to carriage painting, is this putty No. 1. Dry white

SPATULA.

lead, japan and rubbing varnish, the liquids of equal proportions. Probably the best known putty in the jobbing carriage paint shop today.

No. 2.—Dry white lead ¾; keg lead ¼. Rubbing varnish and japan, half and half.

No. 3.—Keg lead, 4 parts; dry white lead 1 part. Rubbing varnish and gold size japan, equal parts.

No. 4, a putty for white work.—Dry white lead ½; pulverized steatite or soapstone ¼; dry oxide of zinc ⅛; dry silica ⅛. Liquids, very pale rubbing varnish ½; light (in color) japan ⅜; turpentine ⅛.

No. 5.—Dry white lead ⅔; keg lead ⅓. Rubbing varnish and japan, equal proportions. Into this mix the woof or fine pickings of velvet or plush. This is especially intended to be used around glass in heavy vehicles.

No. 6.—This is a putty to be used on old work having rough cavities, splintery crevices, and the like. It cannot be sandpapered, but will dry tough, neither chipping nor flaking. Keg lead 1 part; whiting 2 parts. Mix stiff in thick varnish and raw linseed oil, equal parts; then thicken up to the right consistence with dry white lead.

No. 7.—For shallow cavities requiring a filling that dries quick and hard. Dry lead 3 parts; plaster of paris 1 part. Equal parts of quick rubbing varnish and japan.

No. 8.—Deep hole putty. Whiting mixed with raw linseed oil and japan, equal parts. Then into this mixture mix plush woof. Drive a small head tack or two in bottom of hole and then fill in nearly level with the surface with this putty. Slash

SQUARE POINT PUTTY KNIFE.

a couple of openings into it with putty knife to quicken the drying, and then in due time level up with regular putty.

No. 9.—Expansive shallow dents in a carriage surface require a peculiar kind of putty or cement. Finely ground pumice stone 3 parts; dry lead 1 part. Mix to a working condition in thick glue. Apply the putty so that it will show some above the surface.   After 10 hours rub down with lump pumice stone and raw linseed oil.

No. 10.—Here is a putty that will stick and at the same time sandpaper nicely.   Shade dry lead with a little lampblack, and mix with ¾ coach japan and ¼ rubbing varnish, along with a dash of turpentine.

The carriage painter will do well to use sparingly of whiting—even gilder's whiting—in making a putty intended for use upon fine surfaces. Whiting, or, in the speech of the chemist, carbonate of calcium, is a hard drying, tenacious, stout sticking pigment, but possesses the ever present property of granulating and working coarse and gritty under the putty knife.

When coloring matter is added to putty, be governed by what the final color of the job is to be.   Hammer putty well on the mixing block to make it tough and elastic.   Do this at the time of making it and before use in order to expel the accumulated moisture.   Make it in sufficient quantity to last for some time.   Keep the putty in water in a dust proof holder—an air tight one is better.   See putty-holder illustrated herewith.

The way in which putty is applied has largely to do with making it serve the surface good or ill.   Good puttying is not accomplished by nimble feats of jugglery.   The putty knife demands to be skillfully handled and wisely directed.   Putty, in the economy of carriage painting, is quite as indispensable as paint or varnish.   In point of fact, each is dependent upon the other.   Just enough is a critical point in deciding how much and how little of putty a surface requires.   Here are four rules for guidance in the art of puttying:

1.—Never putty on the priming coat.

2.—Putty all work as smooth as possible.   It is economy and increases the chance for producing first-class work.

3.—Avoid, *always,* puttying a crevice, depression, or cavity in the wood, or a joint between two pieces of wood, that is subject to diverse forms of resistance.   The wrenching and twisting of the vehicle will loosen the putty and eventually eject it.

4.—In puttying over nails, plugs, etc., press the pigment firmly into the hole, filling just level with the surface, and carefully slick up all surplus putty.

The painter will need for general puttying purposes, in addition to a spatula or two (which see), at least four different styles of putty knife; one large or wide blade knife, a two-inch blade say, one square point blade, ordinary size, one beveled point, and one oval point.   Knives of different shapes will greatly facilitate the labor of puttying, which at best is often tedious.

SANDPAPERING

If it were feasible, sandpaper would, no doubt, be voted down and out of the paint shop.   At present, however, it cannot well be removed from the system of carriage surfacing. The task of sandpapering, viewed from its rosiest side, is toilsome, dirt-inviting, girt up by a waistband of unpleasant features, but, alas! we must have level and smooth surfaces if we would have beautiful ones, and sandpapering affords the means of getting them. It is one of the aids—one of the great aids, let us bear in mind—to the admirable surface effects sought for in the art of carriage painting. It cannot be slighted or to any extent

BEVELED POINT PUTTY KNIFE.

be done imperfectly without marring the appearance or subtracting from the durability of the surface when finished.

The use of sandpaper begins before even the priming coat has taken its position. A surface well sandpapered ahead of the priming coat saves a great deal of time and leaves plenty of the priming film on the surface where it is needed. No. 1 paper is the proper size to surface the priming coat, if the surface has previously been well smoothed. The No. ½ will do for first lead. This coat requires a very thorough and uniform going over, touching completely all places that need it, touching none with a coarse hand, and never laying bare a flicker of wood needing a full depth of protecting pigment. The second lead, or "dead lead" as we know it, should require only a light going over with No. 0 paper, this to be followed by polishing with curled hair or fine moss used by trimmers.

The rub lead and knifing lead coats usually respond to the smoothing caress of No. ½, or finer, paper, the size depending upon the quality of these coats. All along through the system of painting, sandpaper must needs sound its smoothing monotone, but particularly upon the primary coats does the painter use it as the fulcrum by which, among other aids, he seeks to rear his paint foundation into a tower of strength.

Mouldings, clips, bolt heads, difficult places to work up to, everywhere bespeak the same thorough touch of the sandpaper. There are many sharp edges about a vehicle which may be denuded of pigment at a single rasp of the paper. Such parts require a good measure of protection, otherwise flaking and chipping of the

OVAL POINT PUTTY KNIFE.

paint and varnish must naturally follow. The painter may well strive to make the work of sandpapering an exact operation—exact as to thoroughness as applied to all parts of a surface, and exact as to a uniformity of results.

In company with the labor of sandpapering must be considered dusting. The latter should be cleanly and tidily done, quite as thorough, indeed, as the sandpapering or any other of the operations, all alike important. We now come to an article indispensable to the painter in arriving at a state of perfection regarding smoothness of surface.

ROUGHSTUFF—HOW MADE, APPLIED, AND RUBBED.

Webster defines "rough" as "having inequalities, small ridges, or points on the surface," and "stuff" as "refuse or worthless matter." But, combining the two words into one—roughstuff—the painter construes the term to mean something different from the construction put upon it by the eminent lexicographer when he cleaved it evenly in twain.

Without the coarse mineral pigments known as "fillers," white lead, and the liquid mediums used to properly unite and weld them together and denominated roughstuff when ready for use, the painter, in his effort to make satisfactorily level and smooth surfaces, would be in almost as sorry a plight as the mariner bereft of his compass. For, mark you, gentle *confrères!* roughstuff *is* essential to carriage body surface elegancies and mirror-like effects.

FAVORITE FORMULAS.

No. 1.—To 3 lbs. of any American filler add 1 lb. keg white lead. Beat well together; then reduce to a thick paste with rubbing varnish and japan, after which thin to brushing consistency with turps. This is a safe one-coat-per-day 'stuff.

No. 2.—Equal parts of filler (excepting English) and keg lead, by weight, reduced to a heavy paste in quick rubbing varnish and japan, and then cut with turps to the proper consistency. Two coats per day may be safely applied.

No. 3.—Five lbs. filler (still excepting English); 2½ lbs. keg lead; ⅓ elastic rubbing varnish; ⅔ japan. This is a 'stuff for fine, heavy coach work. Apply coat every 72 hours. Do not rub out under three weeks.

No. 4.—(A London formula.) Dry white lead, ground stiff in turpentine, 1½ lbs.; ochre, or English filling, ground stiff in turpentine, 4 lbs. Mix the two and add ½ lb. of tub lead. Add 1 pint of japan gold size and about ½ pint of the bottoms of wearing varnish. Reduce with a little turpentine if necessary. This is a very durable and elastic 'stuff.

No. 5.—(M. Arlot's formula.) "Grind separately lump white lead with essence of turpentine, and do the same with unwashed yellow ochre; then mix the two pastes in the proportion of ¾ of white lead and ¼ of ochre. Allow the mixture to stand exposed to the air or to a gentle heat in order to evaporate the excess of liquid, and add gradually small portions of good drying oil, taking care to stir and beat the mixture well with a brush, as in distemper painting. The paste thus acquires more body." Concerning this 'stuff the author adds: "It is possible with this composition to give three coats in a day's work, but after the last coat we must wait 48 hours for drying."

No. 6.—English filler 3 lbs.; keg lead 1 lb. Rubbing varnish and japan, half and half, to make a stiff paste. Thin with turpentine.

No. 7.—English filler, mixed stiff with rubbing varnish, ½; japan ½. Thinned with turpentine.

Probably genuine English filler has but few, if any, equals, and certainly no superiors as a roughstuff pigment. It polishes down very close and compact as to texture, giving a glass-like, non-porous surface. It requires less lead than other fillers, because of which property it was specially mentioned as excluded from formulas 2 and 3. It does not surface down as easily as some of the American fillers, a fact that has probably limited its use largely.

In using keg lead for roughstuff, a moderately stiff ground lead is advisable. A lead ground in an excess of oil will necessitate washing in turps to expel a portion of the oil, if the proper proportions of ingredients would be maintained. In mixing roughstuff, it pays to be exact as to proportions and quantities. Use first-class materials, varnish, japan, etc. Slops and refuse from varnish and japan cans are to be avoided. They leave the user in a state of uncertainty as to the composition of his 'stuff. If made in considerable quantities at a time, the pigment should be stored in a tight, dust-free receptacle and well covered with water or turps, else it will very soon become gummy and unsuitable for good work.

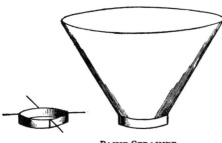

PAINT STRAINER.

The chief mission of roughstuff is to enable the painter to get a firm, hard, level surface. It requires putting on with a good brush, and a skilled and painstaking wielder of the tool. Roughstuff should be carried to a surface a little heavier in body than ordinary paint, but its spreading and flatting property should in no wise be made sluggish and "ropy" by the absence of thinning mediums. Better an additional coat of 'stuff than one coat less because of the excessively thick coats used. Roughstuff, like all quick setting pigments, needs to be applied, brushed out, and leveled quickly under the brush, so that brush marks may not intrude or uniformity in depth of film be wanting. Use a brush suited to the size of the panel; likewise a brush with a softness and fineness of point and sufficient elasticity to insure, if properly wielded, freedom from brush marks. Too heavy a pigment is no more a prolific cause of brush marks than a too nearly worn out brush. If the first coat of 'stuff is laid on the panel with horizontal strokes of the brush, let the second be laid with vertical ones, and *vice versa*. On a well-surfaced job, four coats should suffice. Where greater inequalities of the surface exist, more coats will be necessary. But it is an established maxim in both the practice and theory of carriage painting that the less roughstuff used upon a surface, granted that the quantity accords perfectly with the needs of the surface, the greater the durability of the paint and varnish structure.

The successful user of roughstuff is one who duly considers the importance of having a correctly-proportioned, finely-balanced mixture skillfully applied to the surface amid surroundings favorable to its prompt and thorough drying.

A guide coat to be used over roughstuff is made of a little of the 'stuff colored a bit with yellow ochre or Venetian red and thinned down considerably thinner than the 'stuff, with turpentine.

The workman who has roughstuff to rub requires, as an outfit, plenty of clean water right at hand, a good sponge, chamois skin, and a varied assortment of rubbing stones and bricks. The rubbing brick product, of German origin, has been considerably improved of late years; to such an extent, in fact, that it is now possible to obtain it as fine as wished for, and running from that up to a very coarse quality. However, for the very high class work, the natural lava, or pumice stone, is not to be surpassed. The quality of the rubbing accomplished depends much upon the selection of the blocks of pumice stone. The blocks of light weight, open grain, tunneled with innumerable air cells, are to be preferred for good cutting properties. Immersed in water, they float instead of sinking. The buoyancy of a piece of lava determines its porosity and its cutting power. This kind of stone may be used until the surface is well reduced, when, preferably; the stone of closer texture and tighter grain may next be used and continued in use until the final dressing up has been concluded. Select stones of large cutting surface. After the sawing, filing, and necessary dressing up of the stone in preparing it for the surface, it merits a thorough washing and rinsing to cleanse it from all minute atoms of grit, etc. In the actual work of rubbing a surface, keep the surface well washed to prevent gumming of the stone and to enable the eye to see just what the mind and muscle are doing; but do not flood the work with water. The rubbing stone is doing its work properly when, under an even, gentle pressure, it cuts smooth and free with a clinging, adhesive motion. When a particle of grit becomes lodged under the stone there will be a rolling, jarring motion, easy for even an unpracticed hand to detect, provided vigilant attention is being directed upon the work. When scratching of the surface occurs, the rubbing stone requires smoothing off with another stone, and the surface, stone, etc., given a thorough rinsing with clean water. Circular, zig-zagging motions of the stone are ill-advised. Straight, clean strokes, all directed in one general direction, are best and most effective. A surface is not always rubbed sufficiently fine when the guide coat disappears. The guide coat may be but a mere wash and disappear almost completely under a few strokes of the stone. The disappearance of such a guide (?) coat is not evidence that the proper surface has been reached. By repeatedly drawing the hand, with a good pressure, across the surface at right angles with the direction that governed the laying off of the final coat of filler, the workman can very accurately decide when an adequately fine surface has been reached.

To determine when a surface has been rubbed just enough usually gives the inexperienced rubber no little difficulty, but with practice he will master the accomplishment. On moulded panels it is advisable to rub the edges of the surface first, as it will lessen the tendency to thrust the stone forcibly against the moulding, thus chipping off atoms of stone to be ground into the surface later on.

Rubbing the roughstuff is the final process in the art of developing the comely and durable foundation. Does not the work, then, merit a full measure of skill, alertness, and patience in its execution?

CHAPTER IV.

PRISMATIC AND OBJECTIVE COLOR—HARMONIZING AND CONTRASTING COLORS—MIXING COLORS—TESTING THEM—ASSAYING FOR OPACITY, COLORING STRENGTH, BRILLIANCY, ETC.—TABLE FOR COMPOUNDING COACH COLORS, HUES, AND TINTS.

WHILE colors, as we know them, differ from each other, they exist, according to the generally accepted theory, as simply different movements of the same element. The immense ocean of ether, which is in all space, is one, and the colors are all waves of that one ocean.

When a ray of light undergoes a change of direction it is divided into many minor rays, which to our visual sense are represented as colors. As, for example, if a ray of white light be directed through the edge of a triangular prism so that its course is bent or refracted, the ray is divided into several different rays of colors, these being thereby termed spectrum colors.

It is practically agreed by authorities that the rainbow affords the most complete illustration of spectrum colors, these being formed by the passage of light through the spray or drops of water in a shower. Color, then, may be said to be due to the action of light. Hence the established dictum, namely, white is a reunion of all the colored rays of the prismatic spectrum. It is a basic element in every color except black, and, as a color, black figures as an absolute neutral, it being devoid of white light.

The conditions and circumstances which unite to produce the varying and various color sensations have never yet been unanimously agreed upon by the eminent color theorists. The practical man may thread the remotest confines of color theories as expounded by Newton, Brewster Jones, Field, Rood, Young, and others, until his adventures bring him out on the toil-won heights and stupendous summits of the modern science of colors, and what he beholds will simply tend to confuse his intellect and more than ever convince him that the mastery of color laws remains yet to be accomplished; that no unalterable rule can be successfully applied to the theory of color. To those of my readers who desire to explore deeply into the recesses of color science, I would recommend the works by the afore-mentioned colorists. It is the purpose to deal in this chapter, so far as possible, with the more practical aspects of the science.

Objective color, as distinguished from what is termed illusive or prismatic color, is confined to those substances or materials endowed with the selective property for absorbing the colored rays from the light which is imparted to them, and which, in the technology of painting, are known as pigments.

The colors which make up the three orders usually, but not invariably, recognized by modern colorists, and which practically apply to the needs of the vehicle painter, may be placed as follows:*

Primary Colors	Secondary Colors	Tertiary Colors
Red	Green	Russet
Yellow	Purple	Citron
Blue	Orange	Olive

Carmine, ultramarine blue, and lemon chrome yellow most nearly approach to the prismatic colors, and, taking them for the primaries, we find, according to the deductions of Chevreul and others, that in proportional strength they rank thus: Yellow, the weakest, 3; red, medium, 5; blue, strongest, 8. To form the secondary colors, yellow, 3 parts, and blue, 8 parts, produces green, which is the contrasting color to red, the contrasting primary being always the color not contained in the secondary. Purple, the contrast to yellow, contains red, 5 parts; blue, 8 parts. Orange, the contrast to blue, has red, 5 parts; yellow, 3 parts. Any color in the secondary column opposite a color in the primary column is the contrasting color to that primary, and in the tertiary column, the tertiary opposite any given secondary may be accepted as the harmonizing color to that secondary's contrasting primary; as, for example, yellow, the primary, has purple as its contrasting, and citron as its harmonizing, color. In like manner russet harmonizes with red and olive with blue. The tertiaries may be produced by uniting the secondaries in equal proportions, or by the primaries being combined in the proportion of 2 parts of any given primary and 1 part of each of the two remaining primaries. For instance, olive is made of purple and green, both secondaries, or it may be made of blue, 2 parts, and 1 part each red and yellow. Citron is made from green and orange; russet from orange and purple. Referring to the three different orders of colors, it will be found that experiment will enable one to effect many changes in the development of color harmony. Any one color of any of the three orders will harmonize with the colors which contrast with the remaining two colors of the same order. Take the primary, blue. The contrasting colors to the remaining two primaries are purple and green, with which blue harmonizes. The contrasts to the primaries, red and blue, are respectively green and orange, with which the third primary, yellow, harmonizes. Or red will harmonize with the contrasts to the primaries, yellow and blue, which are purple and orange. Continuing the experiment to the secondary colors, it is found that green harmonizes with citron and olive, the contrasts to the two remaining secondaries, purple and orange; purple harmonizes with russet (russet contains a double share of red, bear in mind) and olive, both being

*With apologies to Mr. W. G. Scott and others who have published similar but more elaborate and scientific presentations.

contrasts to orange and green, the other secondaries. Orange harmonizes with citron and russét, the contrasts to purple and green.

These experiments in the domain of color contrasts and harmony might be pursued indefinitely, but the above will suffice to afford the student who essays the colorist's art (and what vehicle painter doesn't aspire to that art?) a practical working plan for the acquirement of such information as will enable him ultimately to successfully meet the exacting requirements of modern vehicle ornamentation. Knowledge of the harmony of analogy, a simple, effective, and ready way of varying painting, together with a knowledge of contrasts, the finer, higher, and superior system of effecting the most adorable and fetching color adornment, is an indispensable help to the painter, to attain which he can well afford to make many sacrifices.

The harmony of color as it applies to the use of two or more colors with reference to the relationships which should exist between them, requires to be further intensified by a strict and vigilant regard for the season, conditions, and circumstances which obtain when certain combinations of colors are employed. And for this reason: Blue is a cold color, chilly in the extreme at some seasons of the year, upon certain surfaces. It may be called a space color and imparts a retiring effect to form. Red, applied to form, appears stationary and gives a warmth of sentiment. Orange is, if anything, warmer in its effect than a full red. Bright yellow tends to excitement of the vision. Green has a conspicuous or advancing appearance.

The primary colors have no established hues, tints, or shades, but in every compound of the primaries a hue is recognizable. Green, for instance, as a compound of blue and yellow, can be made to vary surprisingly in hue as the proportion of one primary is increased and the other reduced, and *vice versa.*

In every compound of the primaries the predominating primary fixes the hue thereof. Hue, then, as an authority has well said, may be "a mixture of two or more colors of any order, but the mixture should not depart from the original color."

Tone, as applied to a color, measures the depth of the hue of that color.

Dilute a color, or the hue thereof, with white, and a tint of that color or hue is the result. To illustrate: By adding white to chrome yellow, the yellow is reduced along down through the long lists of tints until it reaches white.

A color or hue deepened by the addition of black becomes a shade of that color or hue; or, in other words, a shade is any color made deeper by the addition of black. The positive colors contain no white or black by mixture, while the negative colors do contain white or black or both.

THE MIXING OF COLORS,

in view of the fact that the manufacture of them has now reached a very high state of perfection, would seem to be a comparatively easy matter, but it must be understood that in vehicle painting, business vehicle painting especially, there are many hues, tints, and shades demanded which the color maker does not furnish. Such mixtures have to be prepared by the painter, and the work becomes a skilled operation. First he must be fortified with a clear knowledge of the proportions of the ingredients required to form the desired color or hue thereof, or tint or shade. Then he must skillfully and *perfectly* combine them. The word "perfectly" is emphasized because if the constituents be not perfectly combined, a long train of evils is invited. A most minute and perfect incorporation of all the particles of the paint material must be made, otherwise a lack of uniformity in strength, coloring, and covering power results. Certain colors have a property of unduly asserting themselves when combined with certain other colors in the mixing cup, and if allowance be not made for this assertive strength and a very thorough mixture of the parts effected, the color, when applied to the surface, is apt to show streaks. Some pigments require grinding upon the slab under the muller to obtain an absolutely perfect commingling of the particles.

This rule applies to the mixing of pigments: The more perfect the mixing, the more perfect the product; perfect not only as regards its strength, permanence, and brilliancy of color, but perfect also as regards its working properties.

While two or more pigments may mix nicely together, they may not liquify readily, and unless the workman be thorough in his mixing operations, lack of a uniform film of color ensues, a condition which later on develops the faded and bleached out surface, and in many instances the flaking and shelly one. The painter who would become a skilled mixer of pigment will insist upon exact quantitative measurements of all the ingredients he may employ, both liquids and solids, when such measurements are possible, and he will further see that the ingredients are perfectly united.

The attainment of a high average of results in the use of colors depends greatly upon the achievements of the color maker and upon the uniform quality of his product. Fineness of grinding, uniformity of color in respect to its coloring and covering power, and brilliancy, are valued essentials. It is necessary that the painter should get from the color maker not one, two, or three successive lots of color that are of standard color, tint, or shade, but *every* lot should correspond to the exact standard. When the painter opens a new lot of color, he desires it to be exactly like the last in every particular, provided, of course, the last lot was standard. Hence, uniformity of color, of tint, of shade, of quality throughout, is a requirement with which the color maker may properly be expected to comply. It will thus be observed that the purchase of colors is one of the really important steps leading up to fine and durable color effects.

In testing a color for covering power or opacity, for coloring strength, and for brilliancy, comparison should always be made with a strictly standard color.

To assay for covering power or opacity, weigh out, say 50 grains, of the standard color and the same number of grains of the color under examination, and to each sample add 10 grains of fine china clay, if the colors be dark, or 10 grains of the highest grade of lampblack (this being a pure black) should they be light, and mix intimately. The sample which departs the least from its own color has the best body or covering power. Or mix exactly equal quantities of the standard color and the color to be assayed, in equal quantities of raw linseed oil, incorporating the oil and the pigment thoroughly, and then apply to glass surfaces (small panes of window glass answer the purpose fully), spreading the pigment as evenly as possible. The sample covering the glass most solidly has the strongest covering power.

Coloring power is determined by mixing a given quantity of a standard sample of color with a certain quantity of china clay or, if preferred, zinc white. Of the sample to be assayed take the same quantity of color and mix with exactly the same quantity of china clay or zinc white used with the standard. The sample showing the greatest depth of color may be accepted as having the strongest coloring power.

The durability or permanency of a pigment may be tested by mixing the pigment with raw linseed oil, spreading on a piece of glass, exposing it to the rigors of the weather, and noting its condition from time to time.

The fineness of a color or pigment can be judged by rubbing the material between two thick pieces of glass or subjecting it to a powerful microscopic examination. Or a common fruit can with a tight cover may be two-thirds filled with clean water, half an ounce of color put therein, and the contents vigorously shaken. The finer the sample is ground, the longer the time it will require to settle out.

The following table is intended to aid in the compounding of the principal hues, tints, and shades of colors used in carriage and wagon painting. It would prove futile to try to make the proportions arbitrary, because the uniformity of colors advocated above does not universally obtain, the product of one firm differing from that of other firms and very often, unfortunately, lacking uniformity in itself.

Moreover, color sense has not reached a uniform development, and the proportions which would, for example, make a cherry red as accepted by one person might not appear that color to the second person. However, in most of the formulas proportions are indicated, and the table is presented not as an infallible guide, but more in the nature of a reliably helpful one.

TABLE OF HUES, TINTS, AND SHADES OF COLORS.

REDS.

Transparent Red—No. 40 carmine.

French Red—Indian red and vermilion glazed with carmine.

Carnation Red—Red lake, 3 parts; white, 1 part.

Wine Color—Carmine, 3 parts; ultramarine blue, 3 parts.

Claret—Carmine and ultramarine blue, or red and black.

Imperial Red—Yellow lake, 1 part; solferino lake, 5 parts.

Cherry Red—Carmine, 1 part; English vermilion, 2 parts.

Maroon Red—Lampblack, 1 part; Venetian red, 8 parts.

Solid Crimson—English vermilion, 1 part; carmine, 2 parts.

Superlative Vermilion—English vermilion, 3 parts; orange mineral, 1 part.

Deep Rose—Victoria lake, 1 part; flake white, 6 parts.

Brick Red—Yellow Ochre, 2 parts; English vermilion, 1 part; white, 1 part.

Metropolitan Red—Carmine and vermilion, glazed with carmine. A stunning and saucy panel color.

YELLOWS.

Primrose—Add a dash of white to lemon yellow. Or, according to Standard Dictionary, 58% of white, 24% of yellow, and 18% of green. It should be of a very pale yellow tint; is fashionable and originally English, you know.

Maroon Yellow—Carmine, 3 parts; yellow, 2 parts.

Rich Yellow—Orange chrome, 1 part; white, 6 parts.

Buff—White, 2 parts; yellow ochre, 1 part.

Oak—Yellow ochre, 1 part; white, 8 parts.

Jonquil Yellow—Flake white and chrome yellow, with a bit of carmine added.

Sulphur Yellow—Lemon chrome, 1 part; white, 1 part.

Amber Yellow—Chrome yellow (medium), 8 parts.

Canary Yellow—White, 6 parts; lemon chrome, 1 part.

Naples Yellow—White, 150 parts; golden ochre, 9 parts; orange chrome, 1 part.

Straw Color—White, 5 parts; lemon yellow, 2 parts; vermilion, a drop or two.

Lemon Color—Lemon yellow, 2 parts; white, 5 parts.

Cream Color—White, 5 parts; red, 1 part; yellow, 2 parts.

Cream Tint—White, 150 parts; orange chrome, 1 part.

Gold—White and medium chrome yellow. Add a little vermilion and French yellow ochre.

Pale Orange—Orange chrome, 1 part; white, 5 parts.

Acorn Yellow—White and raw sienna, equal parts.

BLUES.

Changeable Blue—Prussian blue.

Ocean Blue—White, 15 parts; Prussian blue, 1 part; raw sienna, 2 parts.

Ultramarine Blue—Three shades, light, dark, and medium.

Grass Blue—White, 6 parts; emerald green, 2 parts; Prussian blue, 1 part.

Azure Blue—White, 35 parts; ultramarine blue (medium), 1 part.

Cerulean Blue—White, colored with ultramarine blue.

Bird's-Egg Blue—Add ultramarine blue to white until a tolerably intense blue is reached; then give a dash of light chrome green.

Cobalt Blue—A fine pale blue, and a most beautiful panel color. **Very** permanent.

Brunswick Blue—Made in three shades. Popular in some sections.

GREENS.

Sage Green—White, 60 parts; light chrome green, 2 parts; raw umber, 1 part.

Bottle Green—Dutch pink and Prussian blue, glazed with yellow lake; or medium chrome green, 5 parts; drop black, 1 part.

Nile Green, otherwise Body Green—Milori green, Prussian blue, and black, mixed to the desired shade and glazed over with yellow lake.

Tea Green—Made of blue chrome green and raw umber. A striking panel color for business wagons.

Pea Green—White, 5 parts; chrome green, 1 part.

Willow Green—White, 5 parts; verdigris, 1 part.

Grass Green—Yellow, 3 parts; Prussian blue, 1 part.

Marine Green—White, 30 parts; chrome green, 1 part.

Brilliant Green—Paris green, 4 parts; chrome green, 1 part.

Bronze Green—Chrome green, 5 parts; burnt umber, 1 part; black, 1 part.

Scheele's Green—Paris green.

Milori Green—A fine panel color for business vehicles; is rich in color and of good covering power.

Olive Green—Golden ochre, 5 parts; coach black, 1 part.

Quaker Green—Chrome yellow, 5 parts; Prussian blue, 2 parts; vermilion, 1 part.

The greens form a class of colors very extensively employed in the painting of all classes of vehicles. There are two orders of green, namely, cold and warm. In cold greens, blue or black predominates; the warm greens contain an excess of yellow. As a class, the greens contrast with reds and colors containing red, and harmonize with colors having yellow or blue in their composition.

BROWNS.

Olive Brown—Burnt umber, 3 parts; lemon yellow, 1 part.

Bismarck Brown—Dutch pink, burnt umber, and lake. Or, with a mixture of burnt umber 2 parts, white lead 1 part, make a ground, over which put a coating of burnt sienna, and then glaze with carmine, 1½ parts;

crimson lake, 1 part; gold bronze, 1 part. An English vermilion makes a base over which the glazing makes a considerably lighter brown.

Orange Brown—Orange chrome, 2 parts; burnt sienna, 3 parts.

Coffee Brown—Yellow ochre, 2 parts; burnt sienna, 1 part; burnt umber, 5 parts.

Dark Brown—Indian red, 5 parts; Prussian blue, 1 part.

Amber Brown—Burnt sienna, 4 parts; medium chrome yellow, 5 parts; burnt umber, 8 parts.

Indian Brown—Indian red, 1 part; yellow ochre, 1 part; lampblack, 1 part.

Seal Brown—Burnt umber, 4 parts; golden ochre, 1 part.

Tan Brown—Yellow, 2 parts; raw umber, 1 part; burnt sienna, 5 parts.

Japan Brown—Black japan, to which is added a little vermilion.

Umbers—A class of natural earths, affording varying shades of brown, the Cypress mines yielding rich, warm, olive colors. Calcined, this umber reaches a positive violet shade. Burnt umber used alone or in connection with red and black, gives a very striking panel color for business vehicles.

Vandyke Brown—A product of natural deposits of brown color. Vandyke brown is a warm color of a reddish hue and is permanent. Most of the Vandyke browns with which the carriage painter is familiar are made, however, from black, red, and yellow.

Burnt Sienna—A fine, warm, reddish brown, if the sienna be of good quality. A very close imitation of Bismarck brown.

Chestnut Brown—Red, 2 parts; chrome yellow, 2 parts; black, 1 part.

Chocolate Color—A little carmine added to burnt umber.

MISCELLANEOUS.

London Smoke—Red, 1 part; umber (burnt), 2 parts; white, 1 part.

Plum Color—White, 2 parts; red, 1 part; blue, 1 part.

Salmon Color—White, 5 parts; burnt umber, 1 part; yellow, 1 part.

Chamoline (wet chamois skin)—White, 5 parts; raw sienna, 3 parts; lemon chrome, 1 part.

Cane Color—White and ochre shaded with black.

Dove Color—Medium chrome yellow, 1 part; blue, 1 part; white, 4 parts; vermilion, 2 parts.

Fawn Color—White and ochre with a bit of vermilion.

Burgundy—A bright lake given a small percentage of asphaltum.

Silver Color—White, indigo, and black.

Leather Color—Burnt sienna, 2 parts; burnt umber, 1 part; a little white added.

Lilac—Blue, 1 part; carmine, 4 parts; white, 3 parts.

Plum Color—White, 2 parts; blue, 2 parts; red, 1 part.

Maroon—Carmine, 3 parts; yellow, 2 parts. Or crimson lake and burnt umber.

Copper Color—Yellow, 2 parts; red, 1 part; black, 1 part.

True Lead Color—White, 8 parts; blue, 1 part; black, 1 part.

Normal Gray—White, black and purple; or simply white and black.

Pearl Gray—White, black, and blue.

French Gray—White, tinted with ivory black, the mixture warmed with a pinch of vermilion.

Drab Color—Burnt umber, 1 part; white, 9 parts.

Medium Gray—White, 8 parts; black, 2 parts.

Light Gray—White, 9 parts; black, 1 part; blue, 1 part.

Wine Color—Ultramarine blue, 2 parts; carmine, 3 parts.

Blue Black—Ivory black, 15 parts; Prussian blue, 1 part.

Snuff Color—Yellow, 4 parts; Vandyke brown, 2 parts.

Peach Blossom Color—White, 8 parts; blue, 1 part; red, 1 part; yellow, 1 part.

Lavender—White, 15 parts; mauve lake, 1 part; rose madder, 1 part.

CHAPTER V.

THE APPLICATION OF COLORS TO SURFACES.—GREENS—BLUES—REDS— YELLOWS—BROWNS—BLACKS—WHITE.

THE greens comprise a class of colors many of which are leaders in popularity as panel colors on heavy pleasure vehicles, such as landaus, broughams, rockaways, etc. Nearly all the greens are used as solid colors, requiring no specially prepared ground work color. The ease, however, with which solidity and density of color is obtained upon a surface is greatly overshadowed by the difficulty—the extreme difficulty, perhaps I should say—of applying most of the fine carriage greens now fashionable. Such greens as olive, Quaker, Brewster, and Merrimac green, individually and collectively favorites, require very deft and painstaking manipulation in the cup and under the brush in order to insure workman-like results. Probably olive green manifests the most pronounced disposition to assert the strength of some one or more of its color constituents independently and to the detriment of the remaining ones. To overcome this difficulty, the color in the cup should be stirred frequently after having been mixed thoroughly when in preparation for the surface. In applying greens to the surface—and this statement is intended to cover the entire list of greens used in carriage and wagon painting—cross brushing at the final conclusion of laying off the color may well be avoided. The tendency of cross brushing at the ends of a panel is to show two or more different shades of the same green. The rule holds good, when using the greens, to adhere to thorough methods of mixing, to keep the color well stirred in the cup, and to desist from cross brushing at the extremities of the panels in finishing up.

These characteristics so conspicuously developed as opportunity offers have prompted a majority of carriage painters and colorists in our best shops to use most of the greens employed on fine carriage surfaces in the capacity of flat color coats (two coats in nearly all cases covering solid) and then applying clear rubbing varnish, thus doing away with the color-and-varnish coats altogether. The greens which are used as glazing colors comprise ultramarine green, verdigris, and transparent bronze green.

THE BLUES.

Next to the greens in popularity as fine panel colors come the blues, ultramarine blue ranking as the most widely used of the various varieties. The elegance and aristocratic effects obtained by the employment of ultramarine blue are secured only by the development of a ground work free from imperfections. As a matter of fact, the successful use of almost every coach color, whether used as a glazing color or otherwise, is contingent upon the quality of the ground color and upon such a harmonious assimilation of the different coats as will promote the greatest elasticity and permanence. Of the ultramarine blue there are three shades, light, medium, and dark. Most color manufacturers prepare and sell ground colors adapted to the different shades of the blue, the ultramarine being invariably used as a color-and-varnish or glazing coat. Nevertheless, it is often necessary, even if not desirable, to shop prepare the ground color for the ultramarine blues when wanted.

For the light shade of ultramarine blue, Prussian blue and a superior grade of white lead are so combined as to produce a blue of good depth and body, unusual care being taken to have the blue and white thoroughly united and beaten into one indivisible pigment. If keg lead be used in making the ground, the oil should be first completely washed out of the pigment with benzine or turpentine, and varnish, instead of oil, be employed as the color binder. This practice provides for sure and reliable drying of the ground color. The ground for the medium ultramarine blue may be made of the ingredients above stated, the color being simply adjusted to a deeper shade of blue, more blue and less white being used in the admixture. In both the light and the medium, the ground color should approximate the glaze color and enhance the richness of effect. For the dark shade of ultramarine blue, a coat of lampblack furnishes a most excellent and effective ground color.

Probably the richest effect in blue is furnished by glazing ultramarine blue over a ground of very deep green. Transparent cobalt blue, a glaze color always, requires a ground of Prussian blue and white. Body cobalt is used as a solid color, and for a panel color on traps, breaks, and vehicles of that order it produces admirable and fetching effects. The glaze colors are best used in a flowing medium of elastic rubbing varnish, especially when body surfaces are being coated, and the brushes adapted to applying such colors are the 1½-inch and the 2-inch badger flowing brush or a soft, half-elastic bristle brush suited to the size of the panels being coated.

REDS, WINES, AND OTHER COLORS OF THE RED ORDER.

For warmth and brilliancy of color effects, carmine among a long list of gorgeous reds, is without a rival. Carmine is a glaze color exclusively, and the splendor of its radiance is governed entirely by the ground color. Carmine, along with its near relatives of the red order, has a decided tendency to fade, flake, and chip off. The ground color, therefore, must, in addition to being faultless in color density and surface features, be possessed of great enduring qualities. It may be accepted as a rule worthy of practice that the ground colors for the general order of reds should be mixed with a binder of varnish sufficiently strong to impart to them when dry at least a faint gloss—an egg-shell gloss, if it please my community of readers. A ground so prepared is fortified to counteract the fading and flaking properties of such of the reds as are used as glaze colors.

To secure a first-class job of light carmine, bring the surface up level and smooth, and then apply a coat of peach-blow color, made of white and some one of the ordinary reds. Over this apply a coat of deep English vermilion, using the vermilion stoutly charged with rubbing varnish. Polish this coat, when dry, with curled hair and apply a second coat of the vermilion, adding a sufficiency of varnish to convert the mixture to the color-and-varnish class. At the proper time this coat should, preferably, be rubbed lightly with pumice stone and water. Next apply a coat of clear rubbing varnish, which in due time also demands rubbing with pulverized pumice stone and water. Then to rubbing varnish, elastic or quick, hard drying, as the size of the surface may dictate, add enough of No. 40 carmine to fully stain the liquid, say ¾ of an ounce of carmine to one full pint of varnish (many first-class painters use ½ oz. carmine to 1 pint of varnish), and apply to the surface, be it body or gear, with a soft badger or bristle brush. For a less expensive job, omit the coat of clear rubbing varnish and apply the carmine directly to the vermilion.

A method easier to carry into execution in painting a carmine job consists in adding a little carmine to the last coat of vermilion color-and-varnish. This coat is rubbed with curled hair; then carmine is added to varnish, as in the first method, after which a *small* quantity of vermilion is put in to give the mixture opacity or covering power. Clouding and such other incidental imperfections to be considered in connection with the work of one not really an expert in the manipulation of glaze colors, is thereby avoided. For a darker carmine, use a ground of flamingo red, carmine red (a solid color), road-cart red, Kalliston red, or permanent scarlet, dark shade, the latter color requiring a light vermilion ground.

In applying carmine to wheels, it is advisable to flow the whole wheel at once, instead of doing them in sections, as by this practice a cleaner, clearer, and more satisfactory job is secured. For the gear, do the whole of one end of it before wiping up, then the final end, finishing with the reach and side bars, if there be side bars. To obtain the real purple and fine linen of carmine effects, the color-and-varnish requires to be flowed on freely and quickly, and promptly slicked up. Pottering and sectional patching up invites inferior results.

The vermilions, of which there is at present quite a formidable list, ranging from the glaring light shades to the glowing dark ones, all bespeak carefully prepared and durable grounds, if satisfactory wearing and appearing qualities are to be attained. Vermilions may properly, it would seem, be classed among the fugitive colors, and their retention of purity of color is therefore dependent upon the grounds employed to support them. As previously stated, a peach-blow color forms a good ground for vermilion. It should be made to dry with an egg-shell gloss so as to overcome the fading propensity of the vermilion. Then let the first coat of vermilion have a decided gloss. The final coat of vermilion is placed as color-and-varnish. Linseed oil should not be used in vermilion, as it darkens the color and destroys its brilliancy. Ditto japan.

The large class of modern reds known under such alluring titles as C. P. red, flamingo red, brilliant coach red, Ottoman red, Kalliston red, etc., are usually applied over ground colors specially supplied by the manufacturer. With but few exceptions, such reds are used in this way: One coat of color, one coat of color-and-varnish, "dead," or lustreless, coats being carefully avoided.

Indian red in at least two distinct shades, pale and deep, and Tuscan red in three shades are largely used for running parts and panel colors on certain *fin de siecle* pleasure vehicles, and they are painted as solid colors, one coat flat color and one coat color-and-varnish.

In wagon painting, wine colors in half a dozen shades are used. They also need the supporting strength of very stable grounds. Indian red and Tuscan red, of shades suited to the shades of the wine color afford excellent ground colors. If ample time be at the command of the painter, mix these grounds with a binder of raw linseed oil. For hurried work, use a binder of varnish.

Among carriage painters generally, the lakes have never been classed as strictly permanent pigments. At the same time, in the creed of modern carriage and wagon painting they are indispensable. Of those probably the best known in the vehicle paint shop, may be mentioned maroon lake, Munich, carriage part, permanent scarlet, scarlet, red, English rose lake, purple lake, carmine lake, and crimson lake.

Maroon lake is best glazed over a deep Tuscan red ground; Munich lake over extra deep Tuscan red or lampblack; carriage part lake over the same ground as Munich; permanent scarlet over vermilion; scarlet lake over light vermilion; red lake over pale Tuscan red; English rose lake over extra deep Tuscan red; purple lake over a ground made of Tuscan red and Prussian blue. Carmine lake furnishes many of the gleaming and beautiful effects of No. 40 carmine when used over such grounds as are best adapted to genuine carmine. Crimson lake is used over vermilion grounds and furnishes a color of great warmth and richness.

It is advisable, when perfecting the ground for the lakes, to add to the last coat of ground color some of the lake to be used over it, as a mellowing, toning ingredient. The non-elastic quality of the lakes suggests the use of elastic rubbing varnish when preparing the lake color-and-varnish. This will impart elasticity and adhesiveness.

THE YELLOWS.

Among the yellows are many delicate shades which require strong basic color coats to support them properly. In the painting of a yellow surface, be it of the most delicate or the most powerful shade of yellow, the initial coats of color may very correctly be white. Have the surface smooth and clean, and if it be the running parts of the vehicle, and the priming coat is already on, mix the keg lead in, say one-half raw linseed oil and one-half turpentine, using a teaspoonful of coach japan to each pint of the paint. Apply this coat with an oval bristle brush. When dry, sand off lightly with No. 1 paper, putty with white putty wherever necessary, doing the work so smoothly as to require no sanding, and then with a camel's-hair brush apply a second coat of the white containing a strong binder of oil and thinned to a free working consistency with "turps." Over this ground most of the yellows can be brought to the proper depth and density of color with two coats of color and one coat of color-and-varnish. This for the running parts. Upon body surfaces having a roughstuff base, wash the keg white lead free of oil with benzine or turps, adding a binder of rubbing varnish, and apply two coats of the white with a two-inch camel's-hair brush, polishing each coat with clean curled hair. Then apply the yellow, using the final coat in the capacity of color-and-varnish. There is economy of time, labor, and pigment in using a white ground for yellow. Moreover, the natural bleaching propensity of the yellows is distinctly checked through the agency of a white ground. All colors in light shades evince a natural tendency to darken as they fade and lose their original purity of tone. The white ground operates to overcome this tendency, to arrest this deepening process, to hold the yellow to its true color; and it does this by reason of the fact that it offers the yellow a white base instead of a positive, assertive one, to strike through. In other words, the yellow, as it responds to the process of drying, is influenced by the lighter color beneath, the one counteracting the other.

That renowned French authority on coach painting, M. Arlot, is upon record as advising primary coats of white lead as a base for yellows. The writer has personal knowledge of the value of white basic coats for the numerous family of colors in question, and therefore strongly advises their employment. Primrose, canary, and sulphur yellow are among the most fashionable of the pale yellows and require careful working out under the brush. With the yellows must be considered yellow lake. This is used only as a glaze color. Put over the solid greens, it gives to them depth and richness. Placed over Brewster green, for example, it renders a particularly elegant effect. Put over many of the brilliant reds, it imparts a fine and exquisite effect.

THE BROWNS.

In business vehicle painting, the browns receive consideration. Vandyke brown, a warm brown color inclining to a reddish hue, can be used for one coat of color and one coat of color-and-varnish. If desired, a first, or ground, color can be made of drop black, yellow, and red. A close imitation of this famous brown can, in fact, be made of the three colors just named.

Vienna brown, a justly and widely esteemed color for vehicle bodies, is a warm, rich brown and requires a ground color of deep, Indian red. Over this ground apply one coat of color and one of color-and-varnish. This brown is obtainable in two shades, light and deep. London smoke, a much used running part color, is painted solid color—one coat color, one coat color-and-varnish. Burnt Italian sienna and burnt Turkey umber are likewise painted solid colors. As a whole, the browns, as colors, are easily applied to the surface and may be classed as good wearing colors.

BLACKS.

In carriage painting, the black surface fairly reigns supreme. At first thought, the painting of a fine black surface would seem to involve a very common turn of trade craft. It involves, in the largest sense, a high grade of workmanship, rather than a common one, this painting of the black surface. Coach black ground in japan, in which state the carriage painter gets it, should have a binder of varnish, instead of oil, and should be thinned with turps so as to spread freely under a camel's-hair brush and to flat out to a fine, soft, velvety texture. Easy working, without brush marks, is a paramount virtue, regardless of the opacity or covering power of the black. A high grade ivory black is less opaque, and consequently covers less solidly, coat for coat, than does the cheaper, but less lustrous, black. Hence, the covering power of a color can never be accepted as a safe guide to direct the thinning of said color. To make the highest quality of black to cover as solidly at one coat as an inferior grade of black at one coat might, would necessitate using the best black so thick as to invite a disastrous sweep of brush marks. More and thinner coats of color, minus brush marks, are preferable to fewer and heavier coats with brush marks in plenty.

Black color-and-varnish, a popular coating up and surfacing material for vehicle bodies and running parts, is best used upon all the lighter grade of bodies by tipping them so that the side panels at least present a flat, upturned surface, the device, Fig. 9, in Chapter I. of this work, being used effectively for holding such bodies in position. The half elastic brush, flat and chisel pointed, is the most available tool for flowing the color-and-varnish on bodies. For applying the black color-and-varnish to running parts, the camel's-hair flowing brush is an easy and fine working tool and is principally used for that purpose in many foremost carriage paint shops. Like all color-and-varnish, the black variety should be furnished with a ground free from defects, and should be used simply for the enrichment of that ground, to give it depth, density, and an intense jet black color. Such an achievement is impossible through the agency of color coats and clear rubbing varnish coats, pure and simple.

WHITE.

The application of white to a surface and the development of a solid white job thereby is certainly one of the highly skilled features of the trade. The most fitting reference to white would seem to be best made by describing the method used in painting and finishing a vehicle surface in white.

First clean the wood thoroughly, removing all stains, discolorations, etc. Then carefully brush on a coat of raw linseed oil. Seek to have a uniform film of the oil over all parts of the surface. When the surface is ready to recoat, make sure by a careful inspection of it that all parts are sufficiently well sandpapered. Then apply a coat of white keg lead mixed 3/8 oil to 5/8 turps, with a teaspoonful of pale japan added to each quart of the mixture. The second coat of white is best mixed with, say about 3-16 of oil to 13-16 of turps. This quantity of oil suffices to give the white a stout binder without affecting the purity of the white. Puttying and whatever putty glazing is necessary should be done on the first coat of white. Make the putty of dry white lead mixed to the proper consistency in very pale rubbing varnish, 1 part; gold size japan, 2 parts. For stopping holes, the putty needs to be a good bit stiffer than when used for the general run of disfigurements; for glazing, thin to the desired consistency with turps. Sandpaper lightly and then mix Florence, flake, or cremnitz white to a consistency that will render the color free working under a half elastic, soft bristle brush, using turps for the thinner, and hard drying finishing varnish for the binder. Apply two coats of this color, taking due care to have the color laid smooth and free from brush marks. Then take the hard drying finishing varnish and add to it enough of the white to "kill" the yellowish amber color of the varnish, and flow on a full, free, uniform coat. When dry, rub with pulverized pumice stone and water, clean up thoroughly, and apply a second coat of the color-and-varnish. Rub and clean up as before, and apply a third coat. This coat will probably suffice to furnish a solid and pure white surface, fine and smooth, and of becoming lustre. If the job is to go with a full varnish gloss, and striping or other ornamenting is desired, it can be done on this finishing coat, and pencil varnished.

In case gold, silver, aluminum, or other leaf is used in ornamenting, the finish should, preferably, be done in a simple gloss or flat, as it will be found extremely difficult to successfully apply leaf over a finished surface of high lustre. If the finish is to be gloss or flat, give the last coat of varnish adequate time to dry hard, say ten days at least, and then first rub with pumice stone and water, wash and dry up carefully, after which rub with rotten stone and sweet oil, using a piece of chamois skin for the rubbing pad. In rubbing, avoid heating the varnish, otherwise a roughened, shredded surface will result. For cleaning up the oil and rotten stone, dust wheat flour or pulverized slippery elm over the surface, flick off with a soft duster, and wipe dry with a clean piece of silk. In the painting and finishing of a white surface, the subjoined rules hold good:

Avoid using the color too thick. Thinner coats and more of them are best.

After the first, or priming, coat, use as sparingly of oil as possible.   Oil produces "yellowing" of the white.

Abstain from the use of zinc white or damar varnish altogether.   They are alike shifty and unreliable as applied to the processes of carriage and wagon painting.

Care should be observed to keep the surface flawless and perfectly clean. To this end, clean apartments, clean brushes, chamois skins, sponges, etc., may be classed as imperative necessities.

The Florence, flake, or cremnitz white above recommended should be used in the painting of all first-class white surfaces.   Ordinary white lead is advised only when the cheaper grade of white surfaces is desired.

If broad, flat surfaces are to be painted and a strictly first-class job is demanded, a roughstuff will be necessary.   Formulas for roughstuff or white filler are as follows:

Formula No. 1.—Dry white lead, $\frac{2}{3}$; whiting, $\frac{1}{3}$.   Liquids, pale rubbing varnish, $\frac{1}{3}$; turpentine, $\frac{2}{3}$; gold size japan, $\frac{1}{2}$ gill.

Formula No. 2.—Dry white lead, 1 part; pulverized soapstone, 2 parts; pulverized pumice stone, 1 part.   Liquids, rubbing varnish, 1 part; turpentine, 1 part; tablespoonful of gold size japan to each quart of the filler when mixed.

Formula No. 3.—Dry white lead mixed to a thick paste in $\frac{1}{3}$ pale rubbing varnish and $\frac{2}{3}$ gold size japan.   Reduce to a brushing consistency with turps.

Apply one coat of either of the above fillers per day and regulate the number of coats to suit the condition of the surface.   To the final coat add a little lemon yellow as a guide in rubbing out.   A dash of pulverized pumice stone may also be given the 'stuff (especially that made by the third formula) to make it surface free and clear under the rubbing stone.   In rubbing out, "eternal vigilance" and plenty of care and caution are factors of the utmost importance, if scratching and disfiguring the surface would be avoided.   Then over this rubbed surface apply flat coats of the white, reinforced with a binder of hard drying varnish, following with color-and-varnish and other finishing processes as above directed.

While roughstuff must continue to be recognized as a necessity in the development of white surfaces of certain grades, sizes, and forms, the painter, in so far as possible, may well decide to discard its employment solely owing to a lack of durability as compared to the regulation method of building up with color and color-and-varnish coats to a solid and firmly-welded finish.

There is another method of painting white practiced by many first-class painters, which was first published in *Varnish* and written by that reliable and experienced authority, Mr. J. G. Cameron.   It consists of priming the wood with the best white lead, mixed with as much oil as the wood will absorb, and turpentine.   This is given five days in which to dry.

Then white lead is made up to dry with a gloss, and two coats of the mixture is given, with an interval of one day between coats. The surface is then puttied with a putty made of white keg lead, dry white lead and whiting, equal parts by bulk, and japan. The putty used for knifing in is made softer than that used for stopping holes and cavities. The putty is given one day to harden. Then a filling composed of keg lead, 1 part; whiting, 1 part; flour of pumice stone, 1-5 part; made into a stiff glazing pigment with japan and a small percentage of turpentine, is brushed over the surface, a second workman following with a broad putty knife and skillfully removing the superfluous filler. This glazing is intended only for panels and flat work generally. Permit this filling to dry forty-eight hours. It is then rubbed lightly with pumice stone. Moldings and carved work are sandpapered. Next, to 5 lbs. of white keg lead, highest quality, ½ pint of good wearing body varnish that dries quickly and reliably is added. The mass is then thinned with turps and strained. This dries to a little more than an egg-shell gloss. Five coats of this color are applied on five consecutive days, no rubbing or sandpapering being done between coats. This foundation of white is given a week to harden, after which it is thoroughly rubbed down with about No. 1½ pulverized pumice stone. It is then allowed to stand two days before being polished and cleaned up with flour of pumice stone. A coat of high grade and practically colorless finishing varnish (now procurable of the leading varnish makers) is now flowed on and the work is complete. The color for the five coats is made up at one time, so that it dries and hardens equally and uniformly throughout. Mr. Cameron vouches for the durability, fullness, and solidity of a white surface painted by this method, having employed it in painting hundreds of street cars, in addition to a great many hearses, delivery wagons, etc. It is a well-known practical fact that a first-class finishing varnish and white lead carefully mixed solidifies amazingly throughout. And the one coat of very pale or colorless finishing varnish over all produces the effect of a high grade finish.

CHAPTER VI.

APPLYING RUBBING VARNISH—SURFACING VARNISH—CARE OF THE FINISHING ROOM — WASHING THE RUBBED SURFACES—FLOWING THE FINISHING COAT.

ONE well-known varnish maker has said that the marvelous thing about carriage varnish is that it must be one garment suited to all kinds of weather. As a material destined to shine in the public eye, its proper manipulation and treatment is manifestly of the first importance to the carriage painter. No other material with which the painter has to do is so sensitive to the robust variety of influences constantly attacking it as varnish. The virtues of a first-class varnish which add to its durability, increase its brilliancy, and in other ways enhance the beauty of a surface over which it is used are the ones that impart to it a peculiar sensitiveness characteristic of no other material. Briefly, then, we may sum up the task of applying and manipulating varnish upon a carriage surface as a delicate job. A workman of fine notions, intelligent, painstaking and highly skilled in the handling of the proper tools, is the only successful varnisher. Such a workman is required to get all that is true and fine and lasting and lovely out of the employment of varnish. In the varnishing of a vehicle the first kind of varnish we are required to use is rubbing varnish. The duty of putting on rubbing varnish is less difficult, practically considered, than that of flowing the finishing coat, but rubbing varnish bespeaks deft and skillful handling. The first coat of rubbing demands to be applied quite as precisely, and with the same thoroughness as to details, as would mark the application of any of the later coats. In the application of the first and second rubbing coats to body surfaces, the bodies, when of a build to permit of the practice, should be tipped so as to offer a flat, upturned surface, a device for holding the bodies in this position having been illustrated in Chapter I. Fuller and finer rubbing coats may be flowed on when the bodies are tipped. Tipping of all the lighter forms of vehicle bodies is practiced in leading shops when applying the first and second rubbing coats.

The writer, therefore, advises observance of the practice in even the smallest of shops. There is less chance for brushmarks and other defects manifesting themselves. With the heavily flowed on rubbing coats, the round, full surface which distinguishes the product of the best varnish rooms is obtained at a less expenditure of time and labor, than when the thinner coats are employed. I would suggest the full, heavy rubbing coat as the most effective aid in avoiding brushmarks and in drowning out the dust motes and flocculent matter to be noted as part and parcel of the skimpy brushed on coat of varnish. The modern ethics of carriage painting affirms the excellence of heavy rubbing coats of varnish as the most enduring base for heavy finishing coats.

The final rubbing coat may best be applied with the vehicle body occupying its natural position or, rather, the position it is to occupy when the coat of finishing goes on. This is the coat that is depended upon to reflect the outline and round out the fullness of the finishing varnish. The necessity of its being perfect in all the respects that it is possible to make a rubbing coat of varnish, is, therefore, apparent. The fact that varnish goes on

pretty nearly everything, brightens it, keeps it clean and cleanable, covers it, takes the wear, prolongs its life, and increases its beauty and usefulness, furnishes the carriage painter with a substantial reason for insisting upon having his rubbing coats, from first to last, deftly placed and shrewdly balanced.

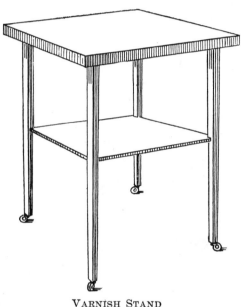

VARNISH STAND
As used in some factory shops.

THE SURFACING OF RUBBING VARNISH.

When a rubbing varnish has been given the full limit of time recommended by the manufacturer in which to harden, surfacing should ensue. To permit such varnish to remain unprotected from the atmospheric impurities common to the average paint shop may be accepted as an actual detriment to the durability of the surface. The gums used in rubbing varnish and which unite to give it a surfacing property render the varnish when spread upon a surface peculiarly susceptible to the attacks of all forms of impurities. Hence the necessity of surfacing the rubbing coats as soon as they have been given adequate time to harden. The supporting strength and ability of such coats are thereby promoted.

To surface varnish correctly and at the minimum outlay of time, it is needful that a serviceable equipment of tools be furnished the workman. This should consist of at least two good pails (galvanized iron pails are probably the most economical), half dozen good, soft sponges, a water tool, and a few first-class chamois skins, in addition to plenty of rubbing pads. Rubbing pads are often shop made from waste cuttings of broadcloth or felt, the strips being rolled into cylindrical form or fastened around blocks of wood. However, the most effective rubbing pads are procurable direct from the manufacturers and come in the form of thick perforated pads, running in thickness from ⅜ to 1 inch, and in size from 2x3 inches to 3x4 inches. These perforated pads serve to free the surface from that part of the pulverized pumice stone which, during the process of rubbing, has become inert and a hindrance to the leveling efforts of the workman.

In surfacing, pulverized pumice stone of the 0 or 00 grade of fineness is best.

The water supply is an important factor in varnish surfacing, soft water being a highly-valued essential. A surface cleans up better with soft water than when the water used is hard. If plenty of soft water is not forthcoming, add a little soda to the water, say a teaspoonful of soda to an ordinary pail of water. This will reduce the harshness of the water.

The actual work of rubbing or surfacing varnish may be classed as an art. The first class varnish rubber is really an accomplished mechanic. Before beginning to rub a surface, first rinse it off with clean water. This by way of a precaution. Then dip the rubbing pad first lightly into the water to moisten it, and then into the pumice stone, thus carrying it to the surface where with light pressured sweeps it may be spread over a certain part of the surface. Rub lightly at first, gradually increasing the pressure until the necessary force is reached. First rub the outside edges of a panel and the mouldings, if any, finishing up the central part last. It will be found easier to get the center of a panel, or of a given portion of a surface, rubbed sufficiently than to get the outer edges of it done. If a large surface is being rubbed, first rub a certain space for a time and then shift to a new space, thus avoiding the possibility of unduly heating the surface. Alternate between the two spaces until the desired reduction of the surface has been reached. Upon surfaces which admit of carrying the rubbing strokes to the extreme end of the panel, the rubbing strokes being always directed lengthwise of the panel, do not cross rub at the ends. Cross rubbing at panel ends is invariably shunned by first-class factory varnish rubbers, and these specialists are deservedly classed as artists in their line. For example, upon piano box bodies the strokes are carried quite to the end of the panel, with no cross brushing tolerated. First coatings of varnish do not invite very close surfacing. The second coat permits, and should receive, the solid and close surfacing. The final rubbing coat should properly require only a moderate degree of surfacing to make it fit to hold out the finishing coat with becoming comeliness. Avoid using too much pumice stone, too much water, or too much pressure on the pad; in a word, avoid excesses. Pumice stone and water should not be allowed to dry upon the surface. It is a hazardous practice. Have plenty of clean water at hand and wash the surface up tidily as fast as the rubbing proceeds. Adhere to uniformity and thoroughness in surfacing. The surface rubbed more closely in some places than in others, and not rubbed sufficiently thorough as to corners, border spaces, etc., bears the unmistakable imprint of the bungler's rude hand. Probably this rule of uniformity and thoroughness is the most difficult for the beginner to acquire. It really covers nearly the whole range of the art of fine surfacing. When one has mastered the feat of rubbing a surface to the same uniform depth of film, missing never a modest slip on molding, around bolt head, or other easily overlooked space, he has earned the right to strive for the expert's rank.

The surface once rubbed, washing up must needs follow. The workman cannot be too greatly impressed with the importance of this branch of the work. Thorough washing must necessarily accompany thorough rubbing; otherwise, the efforts of the rubber go for naught. To insure clean washing of the surface, clean tools must be maintained. The chamois skins, sponges, wash brushes, etc., require storage in some dust-proof receptacle. This may be in the form of a cupboard or small closet, or a bag made of light rubber cloth and provided with a shirring string. Wash these articles often in soap and water, rinsing carefully in clean water after applying and rubbing in the soap. This method will aid to keep them clean. With clean pails, clean water, and clean washing and drying tools, the task of washing a surface preparatory to varnishing is deprived of many of its menacing features. The final washing up should, in every instance, be performed with a pail, brush, chamois skin, and sponge kept expressly for that purpose and used for no other. Always keep in store a sponge and chamois skin to be used especially for washing and drying out the inside of vehicle bodies. Another set, separate and independent of the others, should be devoted solely to washing and drying up vehicle running parts for the varnisher. In cleaning up a carriage body for varnishing, first wash

VARNISH STAND
No. 2.

Standard ½-inch iron, three - pronged and sharpened, 26 to 28 inches high. Quickly made by any blacksmith. Top of stand 10x10 inches.

out the inside surface, tooling out all the corners, etc., with the water tool. Then apply plenty of water to the outside, washing the sill and border of the under surface of the body fully as free and clean as the more exposed parts. Thoroughly tool around all bolt-heads or other parts which offer a lodgment for atoms of pumice stone. After tooling about such surface fixtures, follow immediately with a sponge well loaded with water, thus flooding out the loosened accumulations of gritty matter. The body being finally washed clean, top, bottom, inside, and out, dry up carefully with the chamois skin, and then at once set away in that sacred place, the varnish room.

To summarize the features of surfacing varnish, note: First, Use roll or blocked broadcloth or felt rubbing pads.

Second. Direct the rubbing strokes all in one direction, and lengthwise of the panel.

Third. Avoid excessive use of pumice stone or water, and indulge in not too heavily applied pressure of the rubbing cloth. Moderate pressure, uniformly sustained, is the correct practice.

Fourth. Maintain constantly, and at all times, a conspicuously clean washing up kit; and in washing the surface do not stop short of having it unmistakably and shiningly clean.

Thereby hangs the tale of fine varnishing made easy.

If jobs are rubbed out of varnish and allowed to stand over night before being varnished, a final light rubbing should be given the surface just previous to applying the varnish. A surface when rubbed and stood aside for a short time takes on a scum which, if not removed, is fatal to good varnish-room results. This scum is said to be caused by the oxidation of the floating matter, from the oxide contained in it and the oxygen in the atmosphere. The scum acts in the nature of a deadly blight upon the varnish applied directly upon it, begetting many of what are commonly known as the depravities of varnish. Rotten stone applied and rubbed under a piece of carriage head-lining broadcloth makes an excellent polish to remove all scum from the surface.

FLOWING THE FINISHING COATS.

To accomplish high grade finishing, certain varnish room conditions must prevail. The varnish room must have plenty of light, ventilation, warmth, and dryness of atmosphere. Cleanliness must abound;—personal cleanliness, room cleanliness, and cleanliness of stock and tool equipment. Ventilation and light have already been alluded to. To sweep the varnish room floor, first profusely sprinkle with well dampened sawdust, and beginning at one side sweep in a windrow. Do not use much water upon the varnish room floor, unless it should chance to be a perfectly tight floor and fit to be mopped out occasionally. Then the mopping out should occur upon days when there is to be no varnishing done in the department. A thermometer to register the heat and a hygrometer to register the humidity should be inseparable inmates of the varnish room.

A cupboard set in even with the wall or partition of the room should contain clean cups, strainer, dusters, along with the brushes in their air-tight keepers. Maintain a uniform temperature of from 75° to 80° Fahr.

Insist upon the surfaces and the varnish to be applied to them being of the same degree of temperature. In this way only will varnish work at its best.

Remove the stopper from the varnish can a short time prior to beginning to varnish. This allows for the escape of certain gases generated in the varnish can.

Although the varnish maker may declare his varnishes do not need straining it is really the safer rule to strain all the finishing varnish before using. A majority of finishers in our best shops persist in the practice.

Patent strainers are now on the market adopted for this very purpose. Cheese cloth, cut in squares and drawn over funnel-shaped tins, serves as cheap and quickly arranged strainers.

Be thorough and painstaking in dusting. After the first dusting go over the surface with a piece of silk. Next, give all spots rubbed through, or which promise to show badly under the varnish, a dash of color, immediately slicking these color patches over with a small piece of cotton rag. Now varnish the inside of the body, having previously, of course, rubbed or mossed off this part of the job, as the desired quality of the finish may dictate, and dusted it carefully. The inside surface being finished, again dust the outside surface. Then for the final dusting take a round or oval duster,

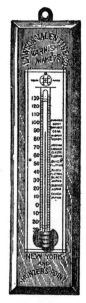

THERMOMETER —
The varnish room
watch dog.

kept expressly for the purpose, and, moistening the hollow of the left hand with a little finishing varnish, flick the point of the duster over this to furnish it with a dust attraction property, after which proceed at once to dust carefully the surface to be varnished.

The surface now being ready to finish, remove the brushes from the keeper, fill the varnish cup one-third full of the strained varnish, and follow this *modus operandi*, assuming, for example, the job to be of the piano box pattern: With the 1-inch badger hair brush lay the varnish along the bottom of the main panel, then across both ends, and lastly, along the top, taking in the seat riser while flowing the top edge. Then with the 2½-inch brush *flow*, not brush, the varnish over the main surface space. Hold the brush, in flowing, rather flat. Keep it well charged with varnish, and pass it lightly and with a steady stroke from one end of the panel to the other, applying and laying off with horizontal strokes of the brush. From the brush held and directed in this way the varnish flows full and rich upon the surface, the distribution being more even and uniform, and less cross brushing becoming, therefore, assured. When the finishing brush is held at a steep angle, or in such a way that the points of the bristles are forced to mainly do the work, the varnish is whipped into motion to a harmful extent, requiring thereby more manipulation with the brush to get it evenly placed, and consequently destroying some of its natural fullness and brilliancy. The chief aim of the carriage finisher is to so first flow his varnish that the minimum outlay of cross brushing and dressing up will suffice, to the end that the varnish may be disturbed as little as possible, thus securing that depth of lustre and mirror-like effects so greatly cherished by all first-class finishers.

In varnishing piano style bodies and surfaces of close kith and kin to such, flow at least one side and an end before cross brushing and laying off.

The varnish, by this method, is given time to take on a bit of "tack," as it were, and in cross brushing a less quantity is removed than would be the case if cross brushing were to follow directly upon completion of flowing the panel. After cross brushing and laying off, "catch up" the edges and all other places where the varnish is liable to start into a run or an overflow.

In varnishing surreys, phaetons, and jobs of that order, and larger, the varnisher should determine the amount of space he may flow before returning to cross brush, by the working qualities of his varnish, room temperature, and the prevailing circumstance at the time of varnishing.

After cross brushing, go over the panel but once in laying off. As before stated, and as expert carriage finishers everywhere will assert, the less brushing and disturbing of varnish, once it is flowed on the surface, the finer the body and brilliancy of the finish.

To become an expert body finisher the workman should possess varnish intelligence. He should know how to keep cool; be an absolute stranger to varnish fright, never lacking for confidence or ability to successfully meet and master emergencies as they arise. The art of varnishing cannot be acquired in a day, or an hour, or simply by a studious perusal of carefully worded directions. These serve as a working draft, but must be supplemented by long-continued practice, and, in case of carriage body finishing, coupled with a natural aptitude for the work.

VARNISHING RUNNING PARTS.

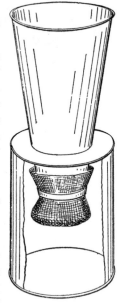

VARNISH STRAINER.

Published by permission of "The Carriage Monthly."

The running parts of a vehicle having rounded surfaces are more easily made to shine fine and mirror-like than are the body surfaces. However, the varnishing of running parts may rightfully be classed a highly skilled operation. Washing up and cleaning the running parts preparatory to varnishing is a difficult task. Around clips, bolt heads, axle ties, etc., pumice stone and dirt accumulations cling tenaciously, and thorough tooling with the wash brush and plenty of water is needed to fit such parts for varnishing. After washing, and once dusting over the running parts, touch with color all reaches of surface requiring it. When color patches are dry take a second duster, kept for this one dusting only, flip it lightly over the varnish-moistened left palm, and go over the surface carefully. If a particularly fine job, pass over the surface with the palms of the hands, having previously given them a slight wetting with the finishing varnish. This method illustrates the power of magnetic influence, and catches up flotillas of dust motes which the duster would possibly disturb, but not remove. In finishing the gear begin at the front axle and proceed to flow the whole front end before wiping up. This gives the varnish a chance to take its position on the surface, and the wiping up serves to level out the inequalities and remove the surplus. After the front, the rear, then the reach, and last the side bars, if any. A brush should be kept solely to wipe up the underside of axles, head blocks, spring bars, side bars, etc. In many factory shops the finishers wipe such parts with the palm of their hand. The varnish drippings are thus caught by the hand and distributed in the form of a glaze to the parts in question.

In varnishing wheels, which are always included in the term running parts, slip the wheel upon the revolving jack and, standing with the left side nearest the wheel and partly facing it, begin by flowing the sides and face of the spokes, reaching the brush well over to the back surface of the spokes. Then flow front of hub. Next the inside and face of the felloe. Now whirl the wheel so that its rear surface takes the place of the front. Catch up and close in with varnish all strips on the rear surface of spokes not flowed when the sides were done. Then flow rear of hub, and lastly, the back surface of felloe. Reverse position of wheel, slick up all places needing it, and set away on a second wheel jack, giving the wheel a sharp spin to better hold the flowed-on varnish in place. Four wheel jacks are necessary to flow wheels properly. Then, when the fourth jack is occupied, the wheel first done, having been given a good spinning and at least three half turns, may be set away in the rack, subject to no danger from runs or sags. When applying rubbing varnish it is advisable to flow not more than six or eight spokes before wiping up. About this proportion of surface for flowing and then wiping up should control in applying rubbing varnish to running parts.

CHAPTER VII.

DEPRAVITIES OF VARNISH : GRAINING OUT—CRACKING—SWEATING—
DEADENING, ETC.—PITTING—ENAMELING, ETC.—SEEDY OR SPECKY—
CRAWLING — WRINKLING, ETC.— RUNS, SAGS, ETC.— RIDGING, ETC.—
PERISHING—CHIPPING—FIRE CHECKS—GREENING—BLOOMING—BLIS-
TERS—SPOTTING, ETC., ETC.

GRAINING OUT.

THE peculiar grain showing a condition of the surface which manifests
itself after the job is finished arises from certain incompetent practices
observed along in the early stages of painting, or from the use of
wood not adapted to the needs of vehicle construction, as, for example, sappy
or unseasoned wood. It is a principle of fine surfacing, substantiated by
experience, that when a carriage body has been perfectly smoothed and
leveled by the woodworker, it should be given a few hours, say four or five,
before priming. This delay is to give the wood, subjected to unusual
pressure during the surfacing process, an opportunity to expand and shape
itself into a normal conformation. Upon high grade work it would be a good
practice to first level thoroughly and set away in an unquestionably dry
atmosphere for a few hours, and then have the woodworker apply a second
sandpapering. Then after another interval of a few hours, prime thoroughly inside and out, top and bottom; in fact, wherever moisture might
possibly find an entrance.

Graining out may come from priming too closely upon the completion
of the woodworker's leveling process; or it may come from the dry wood
having been exposed, after the surfacing process, to a "spell" of damp
weather. The dry, porous timber absorbs enough wetness to raise the grain
to such an extent that nothing short of a resurfacing will restore it to its.
normal smooth and perfect condition again. This wood, with its erect
fibres or grain fairly visible to the eye upon a casual examination, if painted
over and finished, dries out in time, and in doing so responds to the natural
law of shrinkage.

Shrinkage involves a process whereby the priming, roughstuff, color,
varnish, etc., apparently goes in while the grain of the wood goes out.
Graining out is often due to a priming coat that is not given adequate time
to dry hard and firm. This soft layer of rather slow drying pigment, if
sealed from contact with the air prematurely, is a powerful inducement to
grain showing. Spongy, porous roughstuff, deficient in resinous matter and

weak in its binding property, is also often responsible for graining out. Good reliable priming, lead and roughstuff coats, allowed to dry thoroughly, each and all of them, arrest the graining out tendency. Improperly seasoned wood is a prolific producer of grained out surfaces.

Moisture confined under a body of paint and varnish is bound to make its exit right speedily, and this it does by voraciously sucking the paint and varnish material in and pushing the grain of the wood out.

CRACKING.

It has been said that the natural destiny of varnish is to crack. When a varnish has worn itself out, lost its elasticity, become brittle, it will, despite the best laid plans of men and science, fissure and crack. In so doing it simply responds to a natural law. The cracking that occurs prior to this period of service is of supreme concern to the painter. Probably the greatest cause of varnish cracking—the cause that towers above all other causes—is developed by the hurried system of painting—forcing one coat over another not perfectly dry. Imperfectly dried rubbing coats, or a lack of uniformity in the selection of the varnishes used, often cause cracking. For example,

a quick drying rubbing varnish, or a hard drying finishing, even, is employed, over which a slow drying, elastic finishing 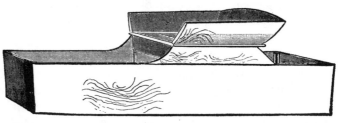 is used. Antagonism between the varnish coats, or between the varnish and color coats; improperly adjusted foundation coats; exposure to sudden atmospheric changes, including excessive heat; the action of ammonia; poor material—all of these are underlying causes of varnish cracking. Imperfectly seasoned panels or moisture penetrating thin wood panels will tend to crack the varnish used over such surfaces. The cracks in varnish due to a continued straining of the panels are termed "force cracks."

Force cracks are usually found just over the steps on the carriage body, running in long, circular lines, also on the panels under the seat riser, and on the seat riser. The vibration of light, insecurely stiffened carriage bodies is generally a direct cause of premature cracking of varnish. The accompanying cut of a buggy body shows the usual location and sweep of force cracks. This class of surface fissures is very easily distinguished from those due to causes previously mentioned.

SWEATING.

Sweating is the taking on of a gloss after the varnish coat has been rubbed. The principal cause of varnish sweating is rubbing it before it has sufficiently hardened.   Varnish laid over a coat of color or of varnish that lacks somewhat of being dry is prone to sweat.   When a coat of varnish has been rubbed and allowed to stand for some time—over night, say,—in a close paint or varnish room atmosphere, it will take on a sort of a gloss or greasy scum which comes under the head of sweating.   It would be in the highest degree dangerous to permanent or brilliant results to flow a coat of varnish directly over a sweaty surface.   The sweat that overspreads a rubbed varnish surface by reason of the absorption of atmospheric impurities can be quickly removed by lightly rubbing with a little rotten stone and water. The sweating out of a surface rubbed before it has adequately hardened can only be remedied by allowing the surface to become hard and then re-rubbing.

DEADENING, SINKING IN, ETC.

This describes a varnish when it goes "flat," loses its lustre, and refuses to shine in the public eye.   The causes of this trouble are, briefly; unseasoned timber, imperfectly dried under coats, such as, for illustration, a four-day rubbing varnish surfaced and finished over after permitting the rubbing only two days in which to dry.   Porous under coats which absorb too great a percentage of the oil of the varnish cause deadening; and porous under coats, let us bear in mind, produce by far the larger share of varnish deadening.

PITTING.

Pitting transforms a film of varnish into an expanse of minute indentations or pits, and simply represents in an aggravated form what is commonly known as pin-holing.   The depravity is caused by a lack of uniformity in atmospheric conditions during the drying process, such as from warm to cold, dry to moist; mixing varnish of various grades; varnishing over a sweaty surface or over imperfectly dried color or varnish coats, or in an apartment having an excessively wet floor, or during a day of unusual moisture.   Pitting may also come from varnishing over a surface rubbed through to the under coats.   Varnish charged with gaseous impurities, or a varnish not sufficiently ripened, is powerfully inclined to pit.   Dirty varnish, sometimes ditto.   Soap or grease smears will cause pitting, as will also too oily under coats.   Draughts of cold air have been known to cause bad cases of pitting.

ENAMELING, SILKING, ETC.

Applied to a varnish surface when it assumes the appearance of enameled leather or silk.   Varnish used upon a hot, humid, moist, sticky day often goes silky or enamels.   Dog day conditions usually invite enameling or silking.   Varnish put on in a cold room is liable to enamel.   Brushing varnish too long, adding turpentine to it, using an oil-saturated brush or mixing different makes or grades of varnish cause the depravities here mentioned.

SEEDY OR SPECKY.

Caused by want of thoroughness in cleaning and dusting a surface preparatory to varnishing. Likewise by the skinning over of a varnish, the broken particles of the skin then working into the liquid and thence conveyed to the surface. Also by using an unripe varnish, or a chilled varnish, or by varnishing on a cold, damp day in a room not properly heated.

The "lousy" or dirty varnish brush begets the seedy, specky work. It is a fruitful cause of such work, in fact.

CRAWLING.

When a varnish, after having been spread upon a surface, contracts, picks itself up into patches, and otherwise vanishes from parts of the surface which should continue to reflect its lustre, it is said to have crawled. Causes: Putting it over a color or varnish ground not quite dry; using oil in the color-and-varnish, or using oil in the color coat to give it a decided egg-shell gloss; handling the work with greasy hands or washing it with water in the slightest degree soapy or fatty. Probably the egg-shell gloss, however, is the most prolific cause of varnish crawling. To remedy this trouble wash the work with clean water, dry off with the chamois skin, and varnish immediately.

WRINKLING, CRINKLING, ETC.

These are caused by putting on a too heavy coat of varnish, or by not dressing it out and wiping it up properly; also by using a varnish not sufficiently ripened. A varnish which shows wrinkling or crinkling while standing in a warm room may be made to assume an aggravated form of the trouble by simply transferring the work to a cold apartment. In the case of varnish wrinkling or crinkling, methods of prevention are preferable to any system of cure.

RUNS, SAGS, CURTAINS, DRAPERIES, ETC.

Some of the causes which develop the depravities outlined in the foregoing paragraph are responsible for those at the head of this one. Other causes are: Lack of uniformity in the application of the varnish, one brushful of the liquid being nicely worked out and the next one being the reverse, or the varnish being applied heavier on one part of the surface than on another, or too heavy a coat serving as the predominate feature throughout. Careless, incomplete wiping up around mouldings, bolt-heads, nuts, and fixtures of that order, generates runs, sags, etc. To reduce these deviltries, first rub with water and pulverized pumice stone. Then pare off a few shavings from a bar of common house soap, dip the rubbing pad freshly coated with pumice stone into the shreds of the alkaline compound, and rub briskly over the offending deviltry. After using the soap, rinse off with clean water very thoroughly. Then rub lightly with rotten stone and wash thoroughly.

RIDGING, ROUGHING.

These terms are given to a surface that resembles a corrugated panel, showing a ridgy, furrowy expanse. Timidity or the spirit of the painter-afraid-of-his-varnish provokes this lamentable surface condition. After the varnish has set past a certain tack and the brush is then drawn through it, roughing and ridging occurs. When one falls heir to this mishap, take a soft badger-hair brush and, procuring a small quantity of turpentine, proceed to apply the fluid plentifully over the panel. This will quickly soften the coat of varnish so that by wiping the brush carefully out, the loosened varnish can be easily brushed off and the surface immediately revarnished.

PERISHING, CRUMBLING, RUSTING.

By this we mean a gradual loss of lustre, the final result of which is a disruption of the surface ending in a complete destruction of the varnish. Washing with water heated beyond the tepid degree is an engaging bid for the disaster here noted. Ammonia fumes, coal gas, salt sea air, soil of limestone localities, etc., cause varnish to perish and crumble away.

CHIPPING, FLAKING, PEELING.

The separation of one varnish coat, or certain parts of it, from another, or from a coat of color is known as "chipping," "flaking," or "peeling." Causes: Moisture in the wood; imperfectly dried under coats; grease and smoke from the smithshop; failure to maintain the proper elasticity between the successive color or varnish coats. It is very probable that the most active and effective cause arises from the use of adulterated turpentine, inferior japan, and a poor, low quality material generally.

FIRE CHECKS.

These consist of a delicate tracery of almost invisible fissures radiating every which way. The displeasing effects of fire checks are not fully disclosed until the finishing varnish has been laid. An extra coat or two of rubbing varnish will usually suffice to conceal all traces of a moderate array of fire checks.

GREENING.

This comes from the use of too many clear rubbing or finishing coats of varnish to a black surface. Successive coats of clear rubbing varnish, capped with a heavy coat of finishing, applied over a black japan ground, affords a pronounced and, in some respects, enticing shade of green. Greening of a varnish surface is also effected by confining the freshly varnished work in a dark apartment while the drying is going on. When the work is fit to remove from the varnish drying room, in order to intensify the greening, it may be stored in a dark room or repository for a time. Recently varnished surfaces held for a few weeks in dark apartments green rapidly. Prevention: Use black color-and-varnish over black color grounds. Add a dash of black color to each of the clear rubbing coats up to and including the final rubbing. Furnish the drying room with plenty of light on all sides, and, so far as possible, insist vigorously upon the necessity of light, airy carriage houses and repositories.

BLOOMING.

Blooming is a whitish, metallic-like film, like unto the bloom on a plum or peach, which obscures the brilliancy of the varnish. It is variously known in the trade as going cloudy, smoky, or foggy. Varnish surfaces exposed to a moist atmosphere, to smoke, or to the fumes of the blacksmith shop are apt to bloom. If the blooming is of recent origin, a thorough washing and drying off with the "shammy" will generally restore the lustre of the varnish. If of long standing and therefore of a virulent type, the only effectual remedy is rubbing with pulverized pumice stone and water and re-varnishing.

BLISTERS.

The varnish surface, dry or apparently so, when afflicted with little eruptions, after the fashion of pustules on the human cuticle, is said to have blistered. The disease is caused by moisture in the wood, exposure to the intense rays of the sun during the early days of service, or to the presence of oil or grease on the surface directly under the finishing coat or between any of the preceding coats of varnish or color. Soft under coats develop blisters, their development through this medium being in this wise: Coats of lead, heavy in body, and perchance a bit fatty or gummy, are applied to the surface. Such coats do not dry *thoroughly*. Oil in color coats tends to the same result. They deceive the workman, being apparently dry, but not really, when choked up under subsequent coatings. A surface so builded is eventually put into service and submitted to the sunlight. Warmed by the heat, these undried particles of color or lead quickly respond to the law of expansion. The varnish, supple and full of elasticity, instead of cracking and splitting into fissures, simply swells up with the paint. Fierce stove or steam heat causes blisters. A varnish blister, if not located upon a too prominent portion of the surface, may be reduced to a surface fracture easily overlooked, by puncturing with a needle and then pressing the rupture down with a wet sponge.

SPOTTING.

There are several forms of this ailment, viz., mud spotting, soapy or dirty water spotting, and the spotting caused by strong currents of air beating powerfully upon the varnish surface. Mud spotting is by far the most malignant type of the depravity herein mentioned. An elastic high grade varnish is more susceptible to the poison contained in earthy accumulations than the hard drying or the low grade varnish.

Accumulations of mud allowed to dry upon a freshly varnished surface spot the varnish through the action of the suction or capillary attraction of the dry mud extracting the oil from the varnish. Again, the spotting may be due to actual saponification, by the alkaline mud, not only of the oil, but of the gum constituent of the varnish as well.

City mud strongly charged with ammonia, and the mud of lime districts, is notoriously destructive to varnish lustre. While it rarely happens that any sort of treatment short of rubbing off the surface and re-varnishing proves satisfactory, the trouble may now and then be effaced, temporarily, at least, by first rubbing the spots with a rag moistened with equal parts of linseed oil, turpentine, and alcohol, and then immediately polishing with a soft piece of blotting paper.

Soapy or dirty water spotting, which may be distinguished by the usually correct circle outline, is difficult, if not impossible, of effacement, especially if allowed to long remain upon the surface, as the potash and acid nature of the water takes a ready and sharp hold of the varnish. A prompt washing off with clean soft water will sometimes prove a cure. This failing, rubbing off and re-varnishing must be resorted to.

The gases generated by an ordinary coal stove or blacksmith's forge, if permitted for long to attack a varnish surface, will effect a particularly grievous type of spotting. This will manifest itself in the form of dull, lustreless spots richly suffused with a film of greasiness. The rubbing down and re-varnishing is the only reliable and sure cure for this depravity. Spotting caused by unusual or disturbing currents of air beating with moderate or fierce intensity upon a sensitive surface is met with in the shape and appearance of dull, indistinctly defined spots, irregular in form, sometimes elongated, frequently of conoidical outline. The first indications of this variety of spotting should be met with a prompt washing off with clean water and a careful drying up under the chamois skin.

CHAPTER VIII.

STRIPING: THE PURPOSE OF STRIPING—HOW TO BECOME A STRIPER—
PENCILS AND THEIR CARE—MIXING STRIPING COLORS—NAMES OF
STRIPES — STRIPING DESIGNS, INCLUDING PANELS AND CORNER-
PIECES—ETC., ETC.

THE chief and essential purpose of striping is to impart a beautifying
effect to the surface upon which it is used. To accomplish this
purpose it must be so perfectly and artistically executed that the

FIG. 1. FINE LINER.

colors employed in painting the surface are made to reflect their most
charming harmonies and contrasts, while the outlines of the surface itself
are cast into more graceful relief. The art of striping, when it achieves this
result, may be said to have successfully performed its office; and the expert
exponent of this art, it need scarcely be added, is accounted an important
member of every well-regulated paint shop family.

To be a really skilled striper, the workman needs to be the possessor of
a steady hand, or, in the words of another, of ''hand magic,'' of an accurate
eye, and plenty of color sense. In point of fact, it is highly necessary that
the striper should be a good colorist; one, in short, who is thoroughly
conversant with the rules of color harmony and contrast.

The first law with which the novice or learner of the art of striping or
ornamenting is confronted is that of color and form. This he must study
patiently and persistently, the while practicing with the pencil in order that
the purely mechanical part of the art be well mastered. Grace, freedom,
sure-handedness, are indispensable factors, as applied to the mechanical
features of striping and ornamenting, and these can be attained only through

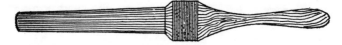

FIG. 2. MEDIUM FINE LINER.

the agency of diligent practice, combined with the help of an eye educated
to act quickly and accurately. There can be no arbitrary rules laid down
to govern the art of striping in so far as it has reference to style. Style is

but the fleeting fancy of "the passing show," and while it is here today it may be gone tomorrow. Hence, the fashion in striping is indefinite and sufficiently elastic to adapt itself to local requirements without departing far

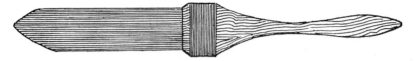

FIG. 3.   HEAVY OR MEDIUM LINE.

from what may chance to be at the time generally accepted as the prevailing style. For, after all, the striping must be subordinate to form, color, and surface, and its lavish or meagre employment, in plain or fancy design, is controlled very largely thereby.

THE STRIPER'S OUTFIT.

The pencil equipment is properly a matter of the first concern to the striper. The last decade has witnessed the retirement, in large part at least, of the round pencils, save when stripes are to be done in sizes exceeding ⅛ in. The vividly sensational name of "dagger" or "sword pencil" has been applied to the pencil which has taken the place of the round liner. Practically all vehicle stripers use these pencils at present. A single pencil, if necessary, can be made to draw a various assortment of lines, running from the hair line to the round line, or even heavier. But, all things considered, the writer deems it best to have a pencil made to draw

FIG. 4.   ROUND PENCIL.
For Stout Line and Round Line.

a certain line and no other. This necessitates the ownership of a larger equipment of pencils, but it also provides for uniformly good work more easily accomplished than can be expected when one pencil is made to do duty in drawing the variously sized lines called for in the average carriage and wagon shop. In Fig. 1, accompanying this chapter, is shown a fine line sword pencil. This draws a hair line when filled properly, and cannot be made to exceed a fine line and do effective work. Fig. 2 is a medium fine line pencil, and Fig. 3 represents a pencil with which a fine line or a round line, or any line varying between these two, may be drawn. The striper should be provided with at least four different sizes of pencils. To make

FIG. 5.

the sword pencil, proceed as follows: Take the desired portion of hair from a large camel's-hair pencil of selected quality, and draw to the proper bevel from one side of the flat portion of the hair. Then, taking the hair carefully

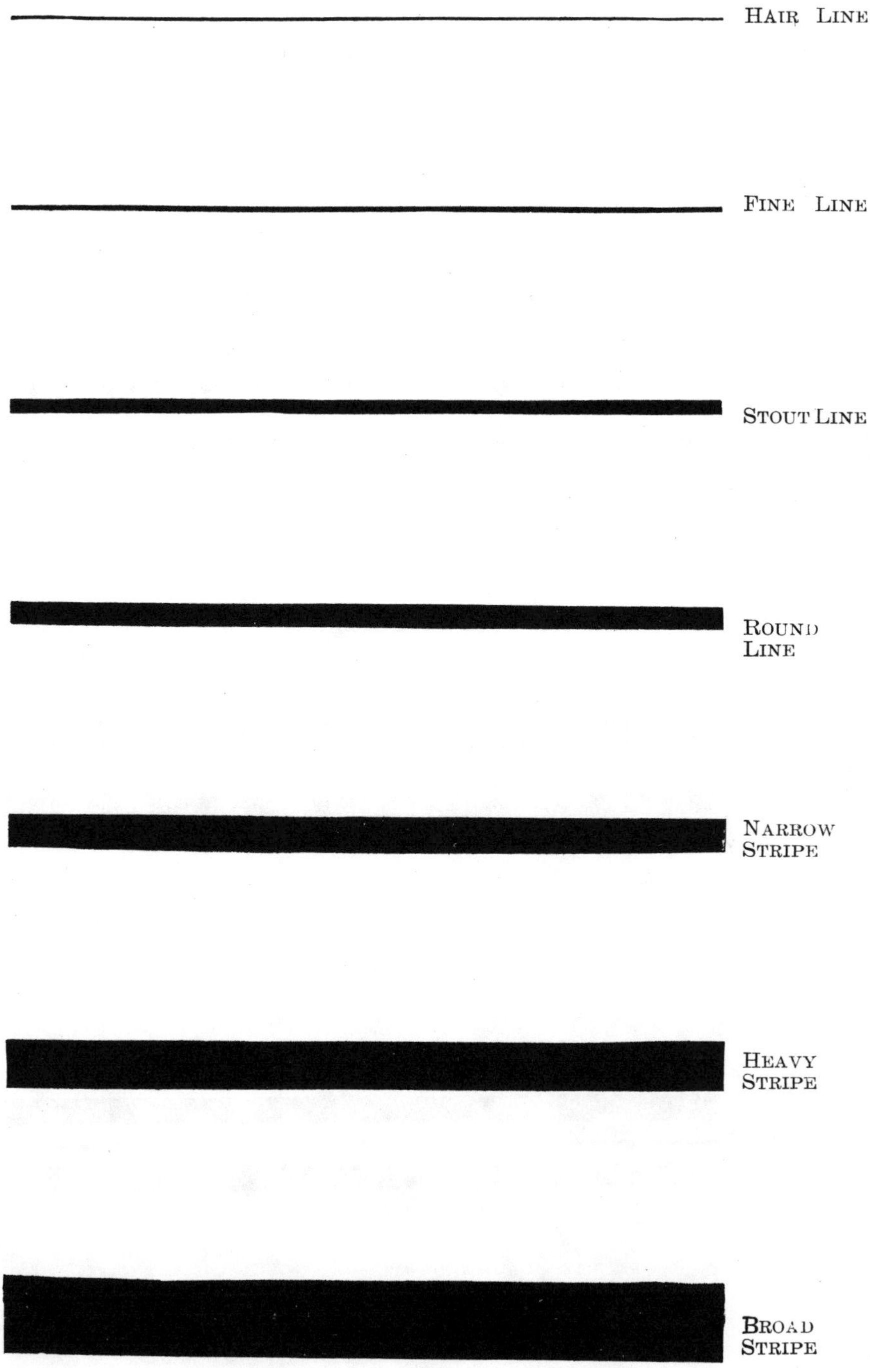

HAIR LINE

FINE LINE

STOUT LINE

ROUND LINE

NARROW STRIPE

HEAVY STRIPE

BROAD STRIPE

COMBINATION LINES AND STRIPES.

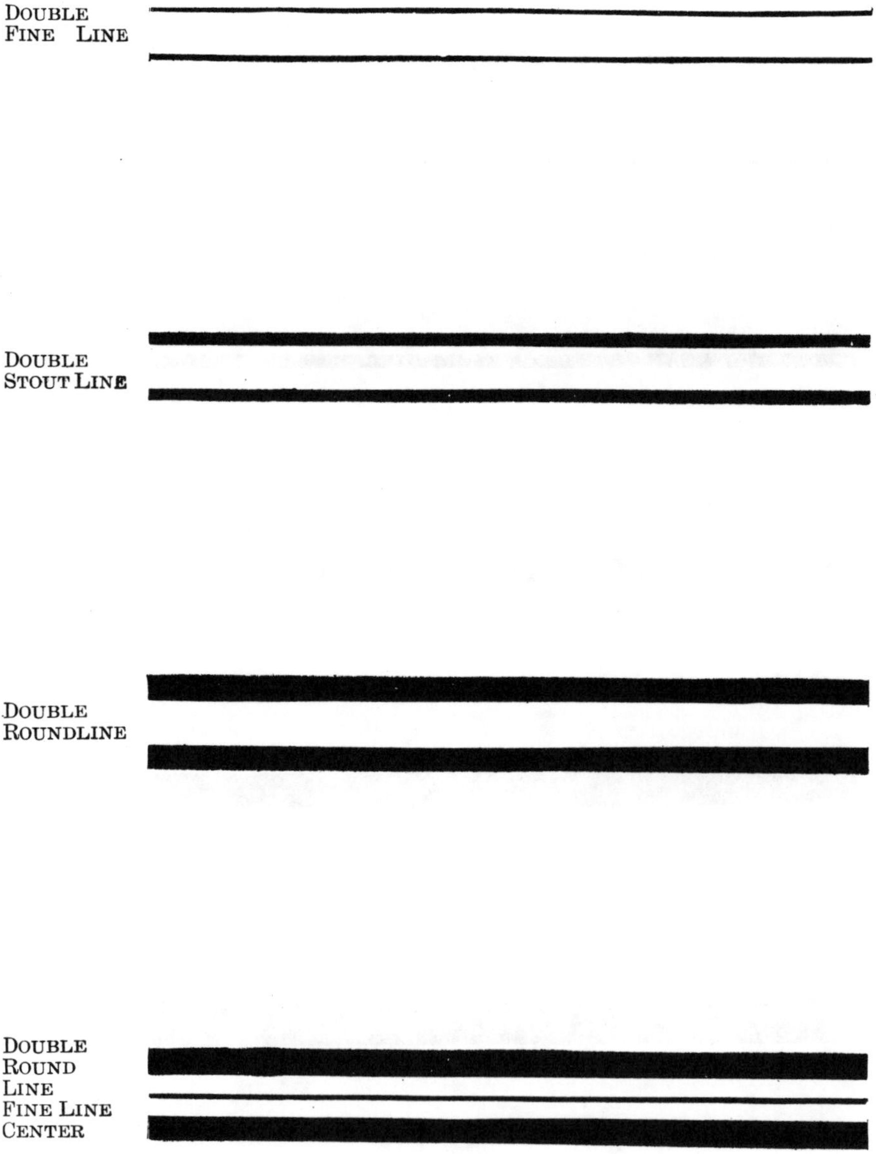

DOUBLE
FINE LINE

DOUBLE
STOUT LINE

DOUBLE
ROUNDLINE

DOUBLE
ROUND
LINE
FINE LINE
CENTER

COMBINATION LINES AND STRIPES.

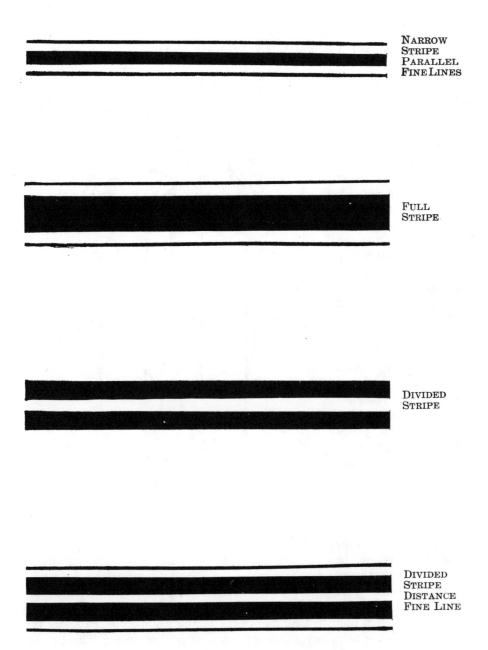

Narrow
Stripe
Parallel
Fine Lines

Full
Stripe

Divided
Stripe

Divided
Stripe
Distance
Fine Line

COMBINATION LINES AND STRIPES.

in the left hand, with the thumb and forefinger of the right hand work a bit of trimmer's paste into the end that is inserted into the handle. Narrow strips of paper, say ¾ in. in width, and of the full length of the hair, are cut and spread with a thin glazing of the paste, and on these prepared strips, about the center of them, lay the hair, keeping it perfectly straight. Next, fold the uncovered portions of the paper over the hair. The day following, or at any time in the future, the superfluous hair and paper may be trimmed from the embryo pencil and a handle attached. A straight-grained piece of pine affords a good handle. Split in center of handle, insert the hair in the split, wrap tightly with stout linen thread, and the pencil is ready for use. In the making of the sword pencil there is often a superfluity of short hairs, of which it is desirable to be well rid. To remove them, take the hair before it is greased, and with the end that is to be bound with the thread held between the thumb and forefinger of the left hand, pull the long hairs over to the right, thus exposing the short and useless hairs and affording an easy removal of them. This process of weeding out the naturally short hair develops the pencil of one length of stock excepting, of course, the desired taper of the tool. While many supply houses now furnish sword pencils of all sizes and lengths, the first-

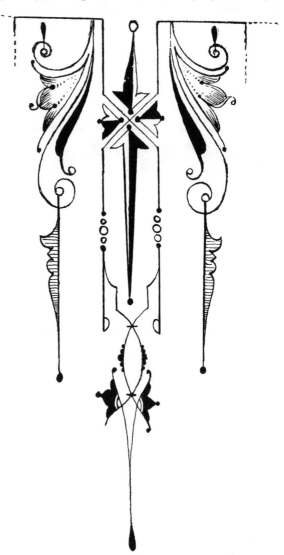

class stripers, the chevaliers of the art, prefer to make their own pencils, and the writer heartily coincides with that preference, the shop-made pencil usually having a poise and balance not possessed by the store-purchased article. To those of my readers who accept the dictum that there is no

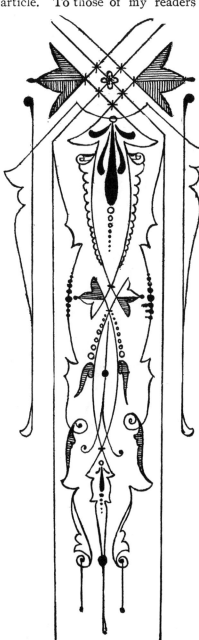

royal road to the art of striping; that the severe schooling in the busy arena of every-day practice is the culture that graduates the talented striper, I would say, learn to make your pencils. Your first attempt, or your second, and perhaps even your third, may not result successfully, but patience and a capacity for taking infinite pains will eventually, if not shortly, win. It is best to make pencils in lots of ½ doz. Two or three out of the lot, even after one becomes tolerably proficient in pencil making, may prove defective. The method of making the sword pencil, as above advised, has the advantage of being easily and quickly acquired, and is therefore recommended to the learner as a feasible one to adopt. With these sword, or dagger, pencils many of the ornamental striping designs which will accompany this and later chapters may be executed, the extreme point of the pencil being used in describing all curves and fancy circles.

To make a round fine line pencil suited to the execution of corner pieces and cut up striping generally, take a camel's-hair round pencil of large size, from which extract the desired quantity of hair. Then cut a small piece of cedar down to about ⅛ in. diameter at one end and considerably smaller at the other. In the smaller end insert a pin until it holds firmly. Then, say, ¼ in. from the wood, clip the pin off. Now shave the stick off until it tapers perfectly down to the pin. Next take the desired quantity of hair, and

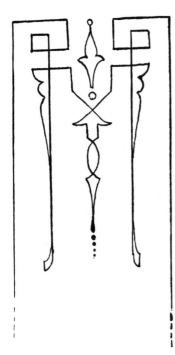

dipping one end of the brush into shellac, lay aside for a few minutes to permit the shellac to harden. Then insert the pin and tapered point of the wood until the clear working length of the pencil measures at least 1½ in. from point of pin. Begin at the lower end of the hair and wind with strong thread up to within ⅛ in. from point of pin. The pin acts in the capacity of a stiffener to the pencil.

The durability and poise and elasticity of striping and lettering pencils depend very greatly upon the manner of caring for them. The striper should provide himself with a dust-proof metal box in which to store his pencil equip-

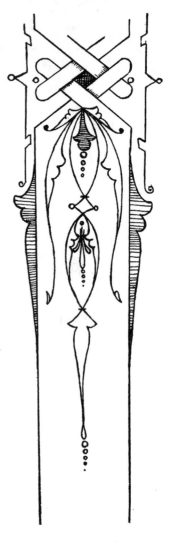

ment. See that it is furnished with lock and key. The local tinsmith will, for a small consideration, outfit such a box with a tin tray upon which the pencils may be carefully arranged. A striping or lettering pencil should be immediately washed out in turps upon the conclusion of the work in hand. Care may well be invoked in washing, to the end that all pigment accumulations are removed from the heel of the pencil. Wipe the pencil dry in soft cotton or flannel cloths and then grease thoroughly, pressing the grease carefully into the heel of the tool. A good grease for preserving pencils in winter is pure lard; in summer, lard and mutton tallow, equal parts. The writer personally vouches for the excellence of a mixture composed of mutton tallow, 3 parts; sweet oil, 1 part. This serves as a good all-round pencil grease, suited to all extremes of temperature, and one the painter will find useful in keeping his pencils in good order.

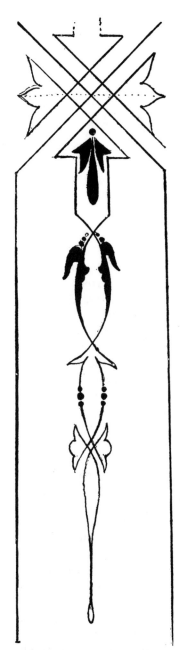

MIXING STRIPING COLORS.

This comprises a difficult and skilled feature of the art of striping. Colors which are worked and controlled easily and dry reliably, are important aids to good striping. Therefore, in order to insure speed, shapely lines, and satisfactory color effects, the striper will find it greatly to his advantage to closely and intelligently study the composition of pigments. Some colors have the defect of being "short." In other words, they do not naturally work freely from the point of the pencil, blotching and flowing out in patches. It is not within the province of the painter to cure this ailment, but it is possible for him to remedy it somewhat. And how? By abstaining from the use of oil altogether, and depending solely upon a mixture of japan, varnish, and turpentine, the proportions of these liquids being governed by the liquids in which the colors were ground. Oil colors in carriage painting are restricted to a narrow margin of use. This specially applies to colors employed in striping, as, save in purely lead colors, the oil has a bad habit of working to the surface of the pigment. When, to meet a certain requirement or emergency, it is found necessary to use oil in the striping color, it is advisable to also add a few drops of quick rubbing varnish as a means of holding the oil in place. White, black, and some of the yellows are usually found under the head of short colors. Flake and cremnitz white are invariably designated as short colors. If such colors are to be used for fine lining, mix with a little rubbing varnish and tint the white slightly with drop black. This furnishes a fairly free working white which shows no laps.

Black may best be described as a riotous, wild-running color, strongly in need of a sturdy steadying liquid. In thinning black to a working consistency, add, say ¼ rubbing varnish. Balanced with this proportion of rubbing varnish, a finely-ground tube black usually works handsomely. The writer would advise mixing all striping colors to the

right consistency in the cups, instead of using them on the palette in a thick paste and thinning down under the pencil as fast as used. Colors furnished with the right ingredients, properly proportioned, the whole being thoroughly united and incorporated, constitute a fine working basis for effective striping.

NAMES OF STRIPES.

In all the foremost carriage and wagon centres the various styles of striping are designated by specific names. This makes it an easy matter to give an order and have it accurately executed without confusion or unnecessary delay. Appended will be found the principal lines and stripes generally employed, the medium lines and stripes only being omitted. As, for instance medium fine line, medium heavy round line, and medium stripe; these being deemed irrelevant to the illustration in hand. The first, or hair, line is the finest line used, the fine line coming next, the line thus gradually increasing iu size until it reaches the broad stripe. What is known as the medium fine line is simply the fine line broadened to the extent of about ⅓ increase in

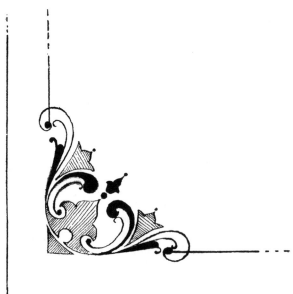

size. The medium heavy round line is the round line with the width `of hair line added to it, while the medium stripe is the narrow stripe increased by the addition of a fine line width. A pencil tracing exceeding ⅛ in. is termed a stripe; less than ⅛ in., a line.

As herewith shown the simple lines and stripes are seven in number, and the combination lines and stripes are presented in eight examples. In the cut of the divided stripe, distance fine line, the

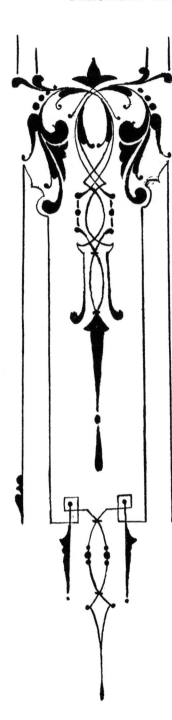

distance line is drawn nearer to the stripe than it is customary to allow. While there is no arbitrary rule to govern the spacing of the distance line from the stripe, it is usually drawn not less than ¼ in. from center line or stripe. Oftentimes, too, it is placed at a distance of scant ⅛ in., as here shown.

The accompanying striping designs adapted to traps, drags, stanhopes, concords, and pleasure vehicles generally (used also on business vehicles) consist of corner and center pieces. Their representation may suggest extensions or changes, through the medium of which a wide variety of designs may be evolved. To specify the colors in which each design is best illuminated would exceed the limits accorded this chapter.

The color of the panel determines the color of the design, or should. A pleasing contrast to the body color should be sought, and in this achivement the workman's taste and art sense must be exercised in lieu of printed directions.

The panel designs, if placed on any dark surface, may be placed in white and trimmed in green, blue, vermilion, etc.; or they may be placed in carmine and tricked out in any of the many neatly contrasting colors. The finest carmine effects are obtained by glazing orange or chrome yellow with carmine. Against the fashionable blue surfaces many of these designs present fetching effects if drawn in gold, white, or king's yellow. Against yellow grounds they may be effectively shown in two or three shades of red. These suggestions apply also, in the main, to the corner pieces. The three last designs on page 184 may be laid in gold, shaded with asphaltum, high lighted with light yellow. The fine lines can be done in any harmonizing color. Some of the small solid parts of these designs can be glazed with carmine and verdigris. Some of the designs may be executed in orange, glazed with carmine and high ledtghi

CORNER DESIGNS.

with chrome yellow. Or the broad portions may be done in some solid color and the fine lines in a slightly different shade of the same color. On blue panels the simple fine line pieces may be done with lining bronze glazed with ultramarine blue; or on green panels use chrome yellow and glaze with carmine.

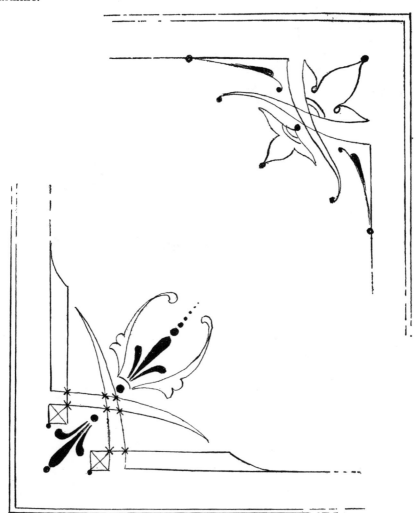

In fact, there is an infinite variety of colors to be used in the development of the designs here presented, and the still other designs which it is hoped they may suggest, the controlling factor in the selection of colors being simply and at all times the color of the surface upon which the design is to be used. In connection with this must exist the law of harmony and contrast, without which any selected color scheme will prove ineffective.

CHAPTER IX.

SCROLLING: RELIEF AND FLAT SCROLLS—HOW TO LEARN SCROLLING—
SCROLLS DONE IN GOLD, ALUMINUM, AND IN COLORS—EXAMPLES
OF RELIEF AND FLAT SCROLLS.

SCROLL painting is a feature of the trade deserving of more than a passing notice; and while it has been permitted to languish in a state of disuse for a decade or more, as compared to its former popularity, there are evidences abroad which point directly to the generous employment of the art of scrolling in wagon painting ere long.

Perhaps we shall never again observe the return of the fine old Roman scroll, bold and imperial, once so common, but a modification of this noblest Roman of them all, or, rather, a combination of this form of scroll and some other forms requiring less space for attractive display, may be expected. Indeed, the modification is already domiciled in the esteem of business vehicle users, being commonly known under the title of composite scroll.

The full Roman scroll, defined as an imitation of carved work in relief, which Raphael and other great masters have so magnificently executed, is of large and shapely proportions, and with its fine sweeps,

SCROLLER'S LINE OF BEAUTY.

graceful curves, beautiful examples of leafing, and endless variety of twists and turns, cannot be confined to a restricted space. It is pre-eminently a scroll of stately style, and amid dwarfish surroundings or when reduced to less than its natural size, its identity is lost and its character as one of the earliest forms of ornamentation, completely destroyed. Hence the modification above referred to.

In learning the art of scrolling, as in learning the art of striping, it is distinctly fortunate to remember that there is no royal road—no mystic method by which one can master the art under the soothing influence of a mid-summer night's dream. The acquirement of the art, as the past masters of the school of ornamental painting understood and practiced it, is the result of patient, arduous practice. For this purpose, a good-sized blackboard is in every way the most desirable surface upon which to work. The beginner should under no circumstances confine his efforts to learn scrolling

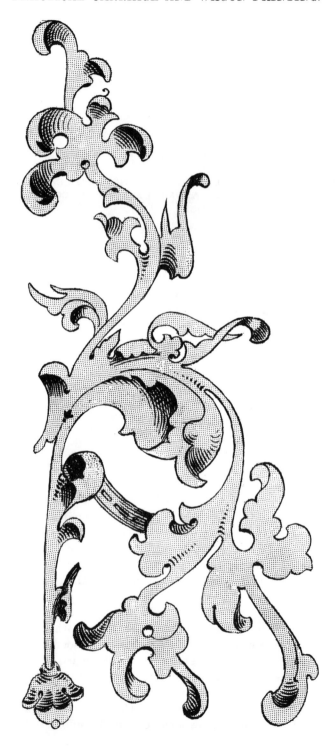

FIG. 4.

to a pad of paper and a lead pencil. As an eminent instructor of the art once declared: "Work with a lead pencil on a 2x4 paper, and the chances are that your scrolls will be of the 2x4 order." Working upon the blackboard with a chalk crayon gives the learner a freedom of reach and a valiant command of the pencil attained in no other way. The easy, free-hand work, although it may be lacking in certain highly desirable features of gracefulness, compels the favorable attention of the critic to an extent of which the copy plate design, mathematically precise in general execution, may fall lamentably short. There is a sort of an indefinable naturalness about the original, free-hand scroll quite foreign to the ornament drawn to rule and square measurements. It possesses a quality that elicits admiration, just as madam's tea gown,

"That floats away where it properly may,
And clings where it ought to cling,"

is looked upon as a dainty creation, wondrous fair to see.

The blackboard and chalk crayon exercise is valuable in imparting to the learner a natural and unstudied twist of the wrist, together with a whole-arm movement that most assuredly must be at the command of the scroll workman. Only by such exercise can the quick, artistic hand be acquired along with an eye trained to correct proportions.

Hogarth's line of beauty can be more expeditiously mastered under the stimulus of blackboard practice than is possible through the aid of most other mediums. Make the figures big and reaching, in sweeps backward and forward, up, down, and in a variety of outlines. This practice will be hard and irksome at first, and, unless one is naturally gifted in this particular line of work, the results accomplished may appear crude and awkward even

FIG. 5.

FIGS. 6 AND 7.

after weeks of patiently applied toil. But in the realms of art few things, to speak in the noble lingo of the Bowery, are "dead easy." Therefore, blackboard work should be studiously adhered to, the work of eminent exponents of ornamental painting studied, as the mariner studies the ocean chart, and advantage taken of all the other aids promotive of a rare degree of skill. The scroll painter able to discard pounce pattern and tape line measurements is licensed to impart a charm and novelty, a

FIG. 8.

grace and variety, to his work, not effected otherwise. The spiral may be termed the basis of scroll work. Intersecting the spiral are the leaves and stems, which, shaded, lighted, and high-lighted, give form and color to the relief scroll.

The learner, having become sufficiently proficient to outline fairly good scrolls with the crayon, should procure some large sheets of paper—manilla paper will do—and paint them in some dark color and then proceed to draw the scrolls with the pencil.

In the matter of pencils, different kinds and sizes will be needed. For laying on the scroll, a black sable hair pencil, the hair set in metal, running in size from No. 4 to No. 8, according to the size of the scroll, and 1½ inches

FIG. 9.

long, is an effective and pleasingly durable tool. For shading purposes a shorter and softer hair pencil is best; say a camel's-hair pencil ¾ inch in length. However, a variety of pencils, both sable and camel's-hair, and of the various sizes, will be found essential in doing the large and small ornaments which the accompanying examples may suggest. Necessary adjuncts to the pencil equipment are, the palette, palette cups, and mahl-stick. An oval palette, made thin and smooth, of mahogany, walnut, or even ash, polished nicely on a shellac base, has for long been popular, and in point of excellence remains unexcelled. Make the mahl-stick of cedar preferably; work it out round and smooth and tip it with a small ball of cotton enclosed in a

FIG. 10.

patch of chamois skin. Taking the accompanying illustrated section of a Roman scroll (see Fig. 1) as a working draft, begin by allowing the point of the pencil to touch the surface and then with a confident, easy sweep twist the pencil around so as to form, say, the first spiral or volute. Next do the stems and off-shoots attached to this volute. Practice to do each spiral, and the stems putting out therefrom, with a single, and at most two, strokes of the pencil. The first principle of fine scrolling consists in getting easy, graceful sweeps, suggestive, perhaps, I may be allowed to say, of the poetry of pencil motion. The tracery of a stilted, cramped pencil sweep is fatal to the balance and grace of a scroll. In practice the student will probably choose gold bronze as the most desirable substitute for gold leaf in working out his gold-finished scroll. The figure, without its shading, affords a flat scroll of fantastic contour, as a draft of Fig. 1, devoid of the shades, will quickly prove.

The shading of the scroll must be done in the same free, off-hand style that must necessarily mark the evolution of the general figure of the ornament. If, as above intimated, the scroll is done in imitation of or in the real gold leaf, the shading is best done with asphaltum, this pigment offering the only true shadow, authorities contend, of gold. Mix the asphaltum with good coach japan and turpentine, half and half. Reference to Fig. 1, and to the other accompanying illustrations, will indicate more accurately than printed directions the parts of a scroll requiring shades. The inadequacy of written instructions teaching the particular portions of the ornament to be high-lighted must be apparent to the reader. Broadly speaking, where the strongest light strikes there high lights should be. For a really practical insight of

this phase of the work the student should study examples of finished scrolls done in the highest style of the art. The gold scroll shaded with asphaltum invites highlighting with white or cream color.

In the execution of relief scrolls it is needful to observe:

1.—All ornaments must have a reason—a useful thing done in a graceful way.

2.—Every line should be boldly, clearly, and elegantly drawn.

3.—Harmony of design, balance of proportions, sympathetic formation of the various parts, demand vigilant maintenance.

4.—Originality of design, with every part having an intimate relationship, an indivisible connection with every other part, is indispensable.

In the execution of a relief scroll, or any style of scroll for that matter, it is a factor of the first importance that the surface be smooth and thoroughly dry.

A great deal of business vehicle scrolling is necessarily done upon the color-and-varnish coat or upon clear rubbing varnish. To prevent the gold leaf (in case gold is used) from adhering to the varnish coat, various expedients have been resorted to, among which the whiting pounce figures as the most effective and the easiest applied. Other recipes include rubbing the surface with a thin solution of starch and water, or glazing it with the white of an egg, or washing it with whiting and water, or applying a thin film of potato starch upon it. Good gilding size is very essential in the art of scrolling. The light and easy whirls of the pencil cannot be done with a size unsuited for the purpose. Moreover, shop requirements have to be met, and they may impose a limit of two hours in which the size must dry today, and tomorrow that limit may be extended to four hours or even longer, and

perhaps—although in these days of ocean racers and Black Diamond flyers this may be a remote possibility—the size will be expected to hold over night, after its application, before being gilded.

Quick size.—Gold size japan, 5 parts; fat oil, 1 part. With a dash of japan ground chrome yellow, this size will dry to safely leaf over in ½ hour.

Medium quick size.—Gold size japan, 4 parts; fat oil, 2 parts.

Four-hour size.—Gold size japan and fat oil, in proportions of ⅔ japan to ⅓ oil.

Over-night size.—Fat oil with a few drops of gold size japan added.

The slow drying size works better and affords a more satisfactory job of gilding than does the quicker mixture, the gold invariably taking a fine burnish over the slow, fat oil size.

The best obtainable fat oil is made by confining boiled linseed oil in a bottle and exposing for a long time to the sun.

To paint relief scrolls in colors is, in some respects, more difficult than doing them in gold or aluminum leaf, and while the radiant combinations of pigments furnish striking effects, there is lacking in the painted scroll a richness, an elegance, an aristocratic display, that constitute distinctive attributes of the gilded scroll. The color of the surface upon which the scroll is to be painted should, of course, govern the color in which the scroll is to be laid. For example: If the ground be a light canary color, first fill the outlines of the scroll with a pale shade of brown. Then deepen the brown fully three shades, and begin the shading of the scroll, blending the deeper color into the lighter so that a gradual melting away from dark to light is the result. Next deepen the brown a shade or two and place the darkest shades, blending them carefully into the lighter ones, but taking care not to extend the blending into the parts previously blended. Next take a little black and run a rather fine line of the color as a shadow to the scroll, the shadow usually being placed to the right of the scroll and at the bottom. This shadow line, to be properly developed, should increase and diminish as the curves and twists are defined. A thin, fine glaze 'of asphaltum is then placed inside the black to shade and modulate it. Some lights of medium chrome yellow are next thrown in, and the high lights following are but a shade or two removed from white. To lend piquancy and a bit of warmth to the scroll, a few touches of vermilion, flicking the spirals here and there but invariably well removed from the lower edge of the pattern, are added. Instructions, however carefully they may be worded, are of but comparatively meagre helpfulness to the novice in painting scrolls in colors. Correctly colored illustrations of scrolls done by such masters as Weber, Kuenzel and Redmond, should be diligently studied.

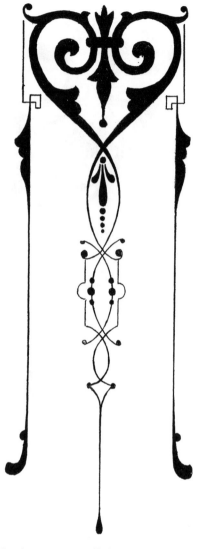

The harmony of colors is the controlling factor in the art scheme of a color-wrought scroll. Once perfectly familiar with this, the ambitious student should encounter no insurmountable hindrances to success as a scroll worker in colors. Referring to the relief scrolls which illustrate the text of this chapter, we would call attention to Fig. 1. If this be executed in gold it may, as previously suggested, be shaded with asphaltum, or asphaltum and yellow lake can be used, and the high lights done in a light tone of Naples yellow. Perhaps the workman may wish to impart to the deepest shading a look of remoteness. This can be done by giving the dark shades a thin wash of some transparent glazing color, as, say, carmine, purple, and crimson lake, or ultramarine blue of the different shades. In Fig. 2 we have a panel design composed in small part of the original Roman scroll and in large part of the more modern style. Lay this scroll

in gold, and then apply a coat of clear rubbing varnish over the ornament before shading, high-lighting, etc. A scroll of this pattern, cast in somewhat delicate outlines, must be very carefully shaded, and if the shading be done over the rubbing varnish, the tendency to cloud and blur will be overcome. In shading, care should be taken to preserve the form and outlines of the design, and this can best be done by making the shade color decidedly semi-transparent. To high-light this scroll, cream, orange, canary chrome, or pure white may be used to advantage. An ornament of this style looks very catchy and handsome done in aluminum leaf. It is strikingly neat on almost any dark ground, with the single exception, perhaps, of black; and it is especially pleasing against the numerous yellows so popular nowadays. Used on the pale yellow grounds, however, it is seen to the best advantage with portions of the design glazed with a wash of verdigris, ultramarine blue, or carmine. The fine line is then done in orange or Tuscan red. Fig. 3 is a rather showy design, of easy form, having for a small space none of the heavy appearance of the Roman scroll. This scroll is intended for the panel of a business wagon. If done in gold, the directions for its execution have already been advanced. The broad line striping environing the scroll gives an admirable effect if done in aluminum. The distance fine line can be drawn in the high-lighting color used on the scroll, or it affords an illuminating effect done in orange and glazed with carmine. The size of the panel should govern the size of the broad stripe here shown. It may run from ⅜ inch to ⅝ inch. Fig. 4 illustrates a corner ornament for a large business vehicle or omnibus panel. It can be laid in gold and shaded and lighted as per directions above. If upon a deep yellow, orange, or buff ground, it can be done to the charm of a rich effect by casting it in aluminum, shading with gold, and picking out with dainty flicks of black. Fig. 5 looks effective on the ends of small panels. On yellow or creamy grounds the fine lines may be drawn in orange glazed with carmine, and the ornaments in aluminum. Shade with brunt umber and burnt sienna, and the shade side of the shading splash lightly with deep blue and the high-light borders with light blue. On dark grounds the fine lines may be done in orange, carmine, blue, aluminum, etc., and the relief ornaments in gold. Figs. 6 and 7, ornaments for panel ends, and 8 and 9, corner ornaments, all light up a surface radiantly placed in gold or aluminum, or they render a pleasing effect done in colors. Ornaments of the order of Figs. 7, 8, and 9 display a dashing appearance done in three or four shades of green against pure white, gold color, light sulphur yellow, Naples yellow, or canary yellow grounds, black shadings being used to touch off the correct effect. Such ornaments, to be sure, when painted in colors should properly be made to respond closely to the laws of harmony and contrast. Too glaring colors or tints used upon goodly sized surfaces are violently detrimental to artistic decorative effects. Fig. 10 is chiefly of the flat ornament style, the center shell only being thrown in relief. This corner piece is done in gold with the shell shaded and lighted, or, as is frequently the case, the shell may be done in aluminum, and washed out with the proper relief colors.

FLAT SCROLLS.

The flat scroll is distinguished from the relief scroll in that it is lacking in all forms of relief ornamentation. The flat scroll is vastly more simple in its working out; hence many workmen essay the flat scroll who under no circumstances would attempt to execute a relief design. The flat scroll is almost invariably first placed upon the surface through the medium of the pounce pattern, and it is then filled in. The design of the flat scroll once laid out on paper, the painter used to manipulating a lettering or striping pencil can readily fill in the outlines. The designing of the flat scroll can best be done upon manilla paper, the tracings being executed with a lead pencil. Then lay the paper over a double thickness of, say, railway car plush and pick out the lines with a small awl. On wagon work the flat scroll put on by means of stencils is not often seen. In the railway car paint shop the flat scroll is usually stenciled on.

Some decidedly captivating examples of flat scroll work are to be observed upon many business vehicles in the larger towns and cities. Many of these scrolls are laid in plain gold or aluminum, in a variety of colors, as well as in colors and gold, and very often aluminum. Frequently the heaviest parts, leaves, etc., are edged with some richly adorning color, and quite as often the veining of the leaves is traced into prominence. The accompanying eight illustrations of flat scrolls, corner, end, and center panel patterns, will, it is hoped, afford at least a helpful working idea of the possibilities of the flat scroll style of vehicle ornamentation.

CHAPTER X.

O F LATE years the art of sign writing, or, in the speech of the shop, lettering, has come to be so generally regarded as particularly distinct and apart from the other branches of painting, having a literature rich and diversified in its resources, that, at first thought, it would seem perfectly feasible and proper to omit from these chapters any attempt to

ROMAN ALPHABET.

deal with the subject. Nevertheless, upon further consideration the writer has preferred to accept the art, for the present at least, as an indivisible part of the carriage and wagon painter's shop practice; and while a thorough exposition of modern sign writing would necessarily trespass immoderately upon the space allotted to the numerous and vitally essential phases of carriage and wagon painting, and cannot, therefore, be entered into, to ignore the branch altogether might fairly be branded as too palpable an oversight to merit excuse. Happily, however, the art of sign writing has been so extensively treated upon in numerous books devoted specially to the subject, and in hundreds of exhaustive magazine articles, that it becomes necessary in this chapter to touch only upon the salient features of the work as they directly concern and apply to the interests of the carriage and wagon painter.

Not later than fifteen years ago the standard styles of the wagon letterer consisted of about five alphabets. The modern sign writer and letterer, encouraged and directed by the forces of recent business development, has to a large extent demolished this standard, substituting therefor what is generally accepted as up-to-date sign writing—a style that readily admits of the employment of whatever form or style of letter will best and most vividly advertise the business it is intended to herald. Complaints have been sounded in widely read publications to the effect that "it was at one time the wagon letterer's good fortune to possess an occupation and a name above that of the sign writer." "His work," we are told, "could be quickly distinguished from the ordinary letterer or sign painter by its boldness and the care given to details. These days have gone by, and we find the well-

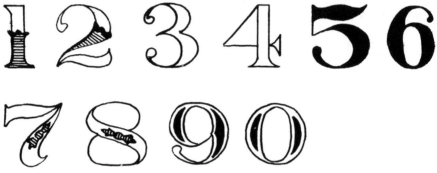

ROMAN NUMERALS.

known and approved style of the wagon letterer prostituted to the idiosyncrasies of house and sign painters."

Such complaints, we are free to say, are in the main exaggerated. The wagon letterer has not been, nor is he in any present danger of being, Othello-like, without an occupation. Moreover, despite the adoption by the wagon letterers of those styles which most completely respond to the dictates of modern business, there still remain certain marked characteristics of the vehicle letterer's work which distinguish it from the efforts of the most finished sign writer. Not that the work of the wagon letterer differs conspicuously from that of the expert general sign writer—the field of up-to-date sign work having merged the two branches into close relationship—but the difference is manifest, as before said, in characteristics most plainly unmistakable. Naturally, this variation should occur.

A sign that would appear legible and clean cut upon a building might, if transferred to the panel of a more or less rapidly moving vehicle, prove unreadable and hopelessly indistinct. A sign attached to a building or other stationary object admits of study from the various points of the compass, from near by or afar off. It is not a fleeting show as in case of the vehicle sign, subject to laws of propulsion which vary to meet existing business exigencies.

Perspective effects, heights, widths, thickness of lines, etc., because of the usually generous sweep of space at command, as secured by the sign writer, do not come within the scope of the wagon letterer's activity, save in rare instances. Ordinarily wagon spaces to be lettered are of dwarfed dimensions and quite commonly cast in irregular outlines. In wagon lettering, whenever possible, the extended letter frequently has the preference. An able and widely observant critic says "it might almost be said that the customary speed of a vehicle can be measured by the degree of elongation which the letterer gives to his work, the lightning express car representing the ultimatum in one direction, while the mammoth furniture van, with its high art panels, is characteristic of the other." The chief

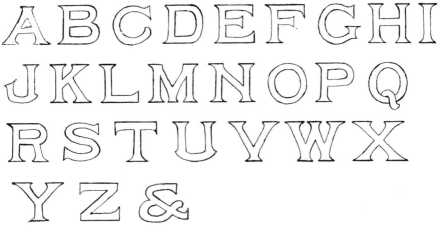

MODIFIED BLOCK ALPHABET.

distinguishing feature of wagon lettering, as contrasted with the average results of sign writing, is found in the wider variety of elegant color effects to be remarked of the first named. The wagon letterer essays glazing with many of the beautiful transparent pigments, and in this wise brings forth charming combinations in color seldom attempted by the sign writer.

The wagon letterer's work is done, as a rule, with quick drying colors or size, and almost invariably is varnished over. Surface smoothness is therefore with him a matter of the first importance. The art of the wagon letterer is composed of many difficulties, each of which must be surmounted ere the learner can hope to stand among the select few and quaff the foam from the beaker of success.

However, let me say that a thorough mastery of the art is worth all the toil, patient study, diligent practice, and applied energy the aspirant may choose to expend.

To achieve proficiency in this branch of painting, it is advisable to practice outling letters with a chalk crayon, or, preferably, pipe clay on a goodly sized blackboard. All lines, straight or curved, should be drawn in free hand, and the practice ought, properly, to be regularly continued until the workman acquires a reliable degree of precision. Ease, freedom, and a masterly command of the hand, coupled with a fairly unerring accuracy of the eye, are justly indispensable accomplishments in sign writing or wagon lettering. Absence of mechanical aids will render free hand and eye work more assured. Many admittedly first-class sign writers practice marking out with rule, compass, and line every letter which they produce, insisting upon mechanical accuracy in "laying out" as the only correct means of developing style. Such workmen, unfortunately, were probably indifferent, in apprenticeship days, to the advantages to be derived from free hand drawing, and being strangers to them they find themselves greatly handicapped thereby.

The free-hand and rule-rivalling-eye mechanic goes to his space to be lettered and after a swift, accurate study of the limitations and contour of

MODIFIED BLOCK NUMERALS.

that space, as a basis for the letter construction, including style, height, thickness, etc., he snaps the necessary top and bottom lines and proceeds to rapidly, but lightly, sketch out his letters. Fairly marvelous examples of this manner of mechanics are to be encountered in sign and wagon establishments. Such men are rarely ever in search of a job. The job is mostly in sharp search of them.

Such skill and facility in execution of lay outs is not gained in a day. An eminent vehicle letterer once told the writer that he "was glad to have acquired the 'knack' of accurate free hand and eye work after *years* of practice." At present there are boundless fields of originality awaiting the sign writer and vehicle letterer. Imitation of the styles of expert letterers may with the beginner lead up to nobler examples of the art—for has not the sage whispered that genius knows only the right of conquest?—but to the apprentice, fired with the sacred spark of ambition, copying will not long suffice.

The acknowledged best examples of sign writing and wagon lettering should serve as the beginner's model, rather than the work of any single practitioner of the art. The fact that the work of every letterer has a certain, positive individuality of style furnishes the best possible reason why the learner should strive to avoid copying continuously the various alphabets of any individual expert to the exclusion of all others.

LAYING OUT, SPACING, OUTLINING, AND BALANCING

of a job of wagon lettering are factors of chief concern. The artistic and really beautiful example of lettering is brought forth only when praiseworthy skill is exercised in executing the operations named. Individuality of work-manship is based upon the style of laying out. A workman practiced in handling a lettering or striping pencil can very soon master the difficulties of painting a letter after it is outlined. The job accurately and artistically laid out, even if lettered in a manner not strictly up to the standard, will far more effectively fulfill its mission as a work of art than will the one properly

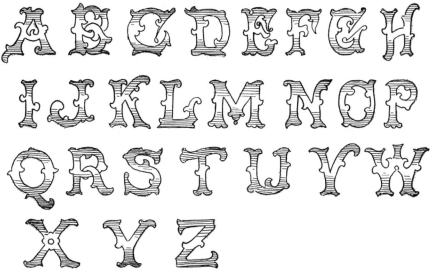

ORNAMENTAL ALPHABET No. 1.

penciled but improperly designed. The key, then, to fine wagon lettering may be embraced in the work of laying out. To present rules by which the workman may at all times and closely abide in preparing a contemplated design for letter painting would be impracticable because the laying out, with its attendant features, must conform to the size, form, and general condition of the surface. In laying out, the best exponents of the art are agreed that it is advisable to employ as few lines as possible. The fewer lines, the more grace, freedom, and easy poise of the letters. At the begin-ning of his career the letterer will probably need the aid of four lines, two for the top limbs and two for the bottom limbs of the letters. As he gains in skill and experience the two inside lines may be dispensed with. Then with the ever present dividers in hand the space so lined out may be "touched off" until the necessary divisions to accommodate the letters desired in the line are spaced. Generally speaking, all letters, except W, M, J, and I, have equal spaces, one square, for example. M and W require a bit more space, I and J a bit less. There is to be remarked a considerable variation in the space between letters, some of the letters being full in form and some open. In the use of L, F, J, A, V, W, T, Y, only half the space given to the other letters is allowable, and in the placing of V and L less than half is permissible, one letter being advanced well into the space allowed the other. The letter I is in some respects a difficult letter to space correctly. When it chances to be cast between two letters occupying full squares each it will require more than the usual space, otherwise, being a needle-like letter, it will be elbowed out of easy location.

ORNAMENTAL ALPHABET No. 2.

The vehicle letterer, daily practicing his art, will frequently find himself confronted with words or combinations of words to which rules of spacing, however carefully they may be laid down, do not apply. In such cases hard and fast rules of spacing cannot be successfully observed. Spacing to suit individual requirements must then obtain. Here a letter may be moved from its nearest neighbor a little more than its ordinarily allotted space would permit; there a letter is placed closer to its neighbor than the rules usually allow. The position of several letters may be disturbed in order that the word or words may display a correctly spaced appearance. Vehicle letterers invariably devote one-half of a letter space to separate capital letters of names. This spacing furnishes the capitals with plenty of prominence and makes plain and distinct the whole name. Usually the half of a letter space is placed between words. This half, however, may vary somewhat as the size and general conformation of the surface may indicate.

In outlining letters many of our best vehicle letterers advise using no inside lines, the extreme outer lines only being employed. This method of outlining precludes the possibility of becoming confused on account of a multiplicity of lines, the spacing may be more accurately judged, and enlarged proficiency in free hand work is attained. Especially in the first draft of a letter design is the use of the outside lines only to be commended.

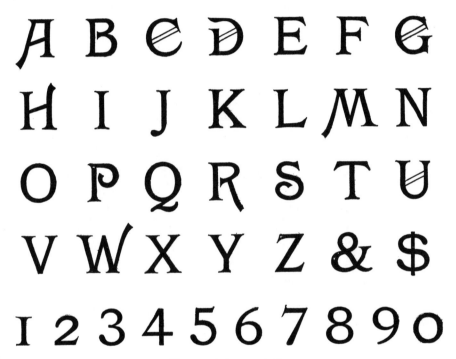

GRECIAN ALPHABET.

The balance of a letter or a series of letters is that effect which gives legibility and artistic proportions to the design. A top-heavy appearance is a fatal defect in a letter. To properly balance a letter is to so proportion it that it will immediately give the effect of being able, if cut out of thick board, to stand upon its base solid, secure, and in no danger of toppling over. For a clearer illustration of the significance of balancing letters, invert some of the accompanying examples of X, S, Z, etc. The base of the letter S, if made the same size as the apex, would throw the letter sadly out of balance. In spacing and outlining a letter design, the matter of shading should be considered, and a needed allowance made therefor if shading is to be done.

SHADING.

Many sign writers contend that shading a letter is nothing more or less than making an artificial representation of a raised letter, and consequently requires a fine light shade upon the top and left side of the letter, and a dark one upon the bottom and right side. Formerly, vehicle letterers did not admit the propriety of this way of shading, insisting that the shades should be on the right side and bottom. Only in case of sunk-bottom vehicles were the shades cast on the top and right side. It was considered deplorably out out of form to throw a shade to the left of the letter.

But the swift tide of up-to-date letter work has left its impress upon the style of shading in vogue, and it is now remarked as admissible to cast the shades at any desired angle and upon any desired side of the letters. Nevertheless, it is the leading custom among vehicle letterers to cast the shading on the right side and at the bottom of the letters. Expert exponents of the

art aver that indiscriminate shading of letters robs their work of its individuality.

Properly, the shade of a letter as it is generally understood may be defined as that letter's thickness or depth. However, that which is strictly and correctly the shade of a letter is the "cast shadow" and it belongs to the side opposite the thickness of the letter. The "cast shadow" usually consists of a thin wash or glazing of the ground color, and excepting its use upon light colored grounds, it is not extensively employed. The wagon letterer resorts generously to letter shading, using single, double, and treble shades, as the requirements of his business suggest. In this work, skill as a colorist of the first order is demanded, a large amount of shading being executed by the manipulation of glazing colors. In double or treble shading it should be remembered that the darkest shade invariably belongs nearest the letter. Moreover, the letter, and not the shade, should display the most prominent color. In respect to letters laid in gold, silver, or aluminum, it is advisable to make the shade touch the leaf. Letters done in pigment are frequently given a "free shade" which consists in permitting a small space of the surface color to separate the letter and the shade. The "close shade" describes the shade that is allowed to join the letter. A shade looks ungainly and ill proportioned if made wider than the bars of the letter, excepting, of course, the treatment of the bottom shades, which are often made a little heavier than the perpendicular ones. This heavier bottom shading is based upon the assumption that the sun casts a heavier shade to the bottom in proportion to the angle of light. While the shading is generally cast against the letter at an angle of forty-five degrees, it is necessarily inclined more nearly to a perpendicular when the bottom of the letter is more heavily shaded than the sides. Some alphabets do not admit of shading, and others require very little, as compared to still others. A portion of some letters in certain styles

of alphabets would present a choked up and inharmonious appearance if tricked out in a shade of uniform weight. Thus, B, K, G, N, S have body angles which do not admit of so heavy a shade as perpendicular or bottom letters. In shading it should be a paramount rule to closely study the tone of the ground, to the end that the most natural shadow be chosen, one that is in strict harmony with the colors of both the lettering and the groundwork. Harmonious and effective color schemes have greatly to do with fine results in the art of wagon lettering.

Gold lettering on black and white grounds may be effectively shaded with almost any color but that of the yellow order. A well-known authority advises the use of the richest and most permanent tones of red, green, blue, and umber shades in shading gold letters placed on colored grounds. Reds, especially the intense and most brilliant reds, are warm, advancing colors for shading gold letters. Imagine, if you please, a more strikingly hand-some combination than a gold letter shaded with red cast against a ground of some one of the fashionable greens. Or reverse the style, and put the gold letter upon a ground of carmine glazed over flamingo red, shading with green. Blue, as a shade, produces a cool, distant effect.

Black letters may be usually shaded with any of the primary or secondary colors. In shading it should be borne in mind that complementary colors cannot always be tastefully combined. As, for instance, yellow and orange would not look fetching to any extent when shaded with blue, although regarded as complementary. The learner should apply himself studiously to the study of happy and harmonious color effects in the matter of shading.

PUNCTUATION.

A staid old axiom has it that "art and education are twin sisters," but the examples of punctuation as seen in wagon lettering often met with

suggest the inference that the vehicle letterer is not slow, at times, to offer a startling contradiction to the axiom. The sense of construction and meaning can be quickly and effectually destroyed in a piece of lettering by a bit of bad punctuation. The simple misplacing of a comma, period, or apostrophe, —about the only punctuation marks deemed necessary at present to bring out the full meaning and make symmetrical a job of vehicle lettering—often results in disfiguring an otherwise really meritorious piece of work. The late Mr. Geo. W. W. Houghton has defined the object of punctuation," to so divide written or printed sentences that the meaning may be made more visibly clear."

In vehicle lettering as now practiced the more striking and illuminative words and phrases are set forth in separate lines, each line, as a rule, carrying a different size and a different style of letter. This system of vividly illuminating and emphasizing vehicle lettering has reduced the need of punctuation to the minimum; but it renders the necessity of a wise and judicious use of punctuation marks none the less imperative. In no way that we are aware of can the information which a line of lettering is intended to convey be so clearly perverted as through the medium of a flagrant error in punctuation. A sweep of lettering done according to the most approved standard of letter form and construction, but improperly punctuated, is at best only a distorted and deformed example of workmanship. The advertising pages of the big magazines offer fine advantages for the accumulation of reliable "pointers" upon the accepted practice of modern newspaper and magazine punctuation. To such sources the reader is invited to go if he would profit by the examples set forth by acknowledged masters of the art of punctuation.

ALPHABETS.

The Roman alphabet is easily the most beautiful and engaging of all the alphabets used by the wagon letterer. It is an alphabet of impressively graceful lines, curves flowing easy rather than exact, with nothing about it

to suggest a lack of freedom or easy repose. The Roman letter, as conceived by the modern school of American sign writers and letterers, is at once the most picturesque and the most difficult to execute of any style known. It is a letter of severe requirements, enforcing in its proper execution a very facile and skilled manipulation of all the aids at the command of the workman. Inferior quality of work cannot be concealed in the Roman letter. Every curve of its noble form must be brought out and fully rounded if the letter is to be what its name implies. Accompanying this chapter is a Roman alphabet, and while there are a number of styles dignified under the title of Roman they are all formed on the same general principle. The Roman alphabet is deservedly held in high esteem by vehicle letterers and sign writers the country over. It is most commonly adapted to the needs of wagon lettering, especially. It is easily read and can be greatly extended, if necessary, without injury to its bold and legible characteristics. The distinctive features of the individual letters contained in the Roman alphabet are briefly summarized as follows:

A has its cross bar drawn at two-fifths of its height. Properly it should be wider than the H or N. The center bar of B belongs above the center of the letter. C is not drawn in a perfect circle. Abrupt curves should be avoided and the exact lines of the dividers discarded. D requires care in execution, its large sweeping curve being a difficult one to control. E goes a bit wider than its height, with bar above center. F is frequently drawn a trifle narrower than E. Remarks made concerning C apply to G. Keep cross bar of H above the center. Its width should be about equal to its

height. I is very easy to make and needs no description. J is a little narrower than the other letters. K is entitled to about the same space as H. The cut shows where the angles of the letter meet. L and M occupy considerably more space than other letters. N requires the same space as H. O is a little wider than C. The necessity for this increased width will become immediately plain to one who will first make C and then undertake to confine O in the same circle. The proportion of P is shown in the alphabet. Q, along with O, needs easy, sweeping curves to best display its form. Make the appendage clean cut and bold. It has been said that a wagon letterer's standard as an artist is determined by the quality of his Roman

R's. Be that as it may, R is rightfully regarded as a difficult letter to execute. The cross bar usually goes in at the center of the letter. The tail of the letter constitutes the difficult point to control. S is a handsome letter, withal a difficult one to execute properly. To ascertain the correctness of one's S, invert the letter as drawn. Inverted the letter will be top-heavy but it should not be built on awkward lines. T has the same height as width. It should not be narrowed beyond the proportion here indicated, as one often observes it in sign work. N and V may be passed without comment. W, practically composed of two V's, is distinguished as the widest letter of the alphabet. X occupies about the usual space and its upper part should be smaller than the nether. Y is best known as a wide letter and like the T, has a shape that tends to break the regularity of spacing and leads the workman oftentimes to ruin the appearance of the letter through the process of contraction. Z is ordinarily classed as one of the easy letters of the alphabet to make.

The modified block alphabet herewith shown is executed by many Eastern wagon letterers, and it may be said to be drawn upon pleasing and easy lines. In display lines the modified block presents a glowingly fine appearance, forcible, prominent, and plain enough for him who runs to read.

The ornamental alphabets set forth in alphabets No. 1 and No. 2 require no extended comment. They may be varied somewhat to meet certain needs and necessities. The letters composing No. 2 have limbs projecting above and below the regulation lines, and therein lies the chief beauty.

By the kind permission of Mr. Chas. B. Sherron, editor of *Varnish*, the writer is pleased to illustrate a Grecian alphabet of decidedly unique attractions. Wagon letterers have come to regard this alphabet with much favor, and, if properly executed, it gives very striking effects. The embellishments admit of innumerable changes and modifications. In point of fact, the variations that are possible with this design are only limited by the talent of the workman. The letters may be shaded quite as handily as other styles. Done in gold against any dark ground they furnish beautiful and rich effects.

Accompanying these alphabets are a few designs for business vehicle panels in which examples of present day lettering are reflected from variously ornamented grounds. From a study of them the apprentice may perhaps find a suggestion that will lead him to originate more pretentious examples. There are many unexplored fields of beauty in the domain of ornamental wagon lettering, bear in mind.

CHAPTER XI.

MONOGRAMS — ANTIQUITY OF THE MONOGRAM — HOW TO DESIGN AND PAINT THE MONOGRAM — TOOLS NEEDED—LEADING COLORS EM-PLOYED—SOME ENGAGING COMBINATIONS—ILLUSTRATIONS, ETC.

THE designing and painting of monograms is an accomplishment which the carriage painter should zealously strive to acquire. Years ago the crest, coat-of-arms, and other elaborate forms of ornamentation accompanied the monogram in its mission as a panel decoration. Gradually, in response to the dictates of the vehicle-using public, and encouraged, no doubt, by the stern mandates of competition, the use of the lavishly wrought style of panel ornament has given way largely to the monogram. Despite the apparent tendency toward plain effects in the matter of pleasure

vehicle ornamentation the fact remains unassailed that a well executed monogram cast upon the panels of a vehicle imparts a color effect, and breaks the monotony of a finish, to a very satisfying extent. As my lamented friend Manchester was won't to say: "That little patch of color warms up the entire job, relieving that sense of same-ness that one feels when contemplating a carriage. No matter how nicely it is fin-ished, there seems to be something lacking if the ornament is omitted. That little color spot is like an oasis in a desert—a resting place, as it were, for the eye." Most certain it is that the dull uniformity, the eye offending lack of variety, in the painting of a carriage panel is often relieved by the simple addition of a monogram. The monogram is not of recent origin. Away back in those alluring days of Greek heroes and Egyptian divinities the monogram existed. Indeed, early in the fourth century, as ancient history informs us, monograms were used to identify the pomp of power. In France the monogram was early employed in the capacity of a signature and inscribed upon seals and coins. In point of fact, the use and purpose of the monogram was clearly established when the world was yet young.

The word monogram is said to be derived from two modest little Greek words, *monos*, alone, only, and *gramma*, letter. Authorities differ considerably in defining the word monogram. A modern authority refers to it in this wise: "In the true monogram two of its letters, or all, for that matter,

should have some portion in common." Again it is said to consist of "characters or ciphers composed of two or more letters interwoven, being an abbreviation of a name." Still another authority contends that the monogram is "a device formed by the assemblage of two or more letters so as to form a single character." Probably the three definitions here quoted determine the limits and significance of the monogram as we wish to know it today. If the monogram is formed of but two letters it is denominated a simple monogram. Composed of all the letters of a name it is classified as a complete monogram. It is not the writer's purpose to inveigh against the elaborate and complicated monogram, which, in some respects, at least, partakes freely of the mystifying characteristics of an oriental newspaper advertisement, but he does wish to emphasize the value of a monogram devoted to the use of vehicular adornment made sufficiently plain and simple to be easily read by one not used to deciphering hieroglyphics. "Handsome is that handsome does," runs the quaint old axiom, and, generally speaking, the clean cut, unimcumbered, legible monogram, serves its office as a handsome ornament when it offers to the observer a tale soon told.

The designing and painting of monograms constitutes an art mastered, save in exceptional instances, only after long continued study and practice. Some of our best monogram makers do not ascribe their success to talent, but, rather, to hard work and practice. Works on monograms furnish plenty of examples of the different styles (which consist, principally, of the Florentine, script, and block,) for the guidance of the beginner. With such examples before him the work of making monograms may be

begun. Mr. W. A. Thompson, probably one of the most skillful monogram designers in the country, advises the student to "begin practice with a slate and pencil for a time at least, as the lines can be more readily erased than from paper.'' As some proficiency is gained the slate may be discarded in

O. D. T.

favor of the writing pad, pencil and eraser. The compass and dividers are not advised as aids to be constantly relied upon. The general practice should be to let these aids severely alone. Free-hand drawing produces, as a rule, the most symmetrical and graceful monogram. Study of proportion and balance should early engage the thought of the learner. Curves on one side of a monogram, for instance, should be followed when possible by similar ones on the opposite side. Also, as a rule, the base should be a little sturdier than the apex. It would prove futile to attempt to append any set of rules to govern the designing of a monogram. The principle that would obtain in the laying out of one design would probably fail of being a principle at all in the drawing of the second one. This by virtue of the law of variation which rules in this as in all other arts. The letter delected from its true course, (its stand-considered,) either one as a matter of balance, swung in an opposite possible at all times to which admit of an ex-problem of balance and an easy solution. But not the case. Hence,

W. H. D.

ing alone not being here way or the other, should, be matched by a letter direction. If it were use only those letters quisite arrangement, the proportion would invite such, unfortunately, is the charm and beauty of

the monogram must necessarily be governed at times by the individual letters of which it is composed instead of by their arrangement *en masse*. The perfectly symmetrical monogram is not always possible under the masterful touch of the most dashing originator of monogram architecture.

In designing a monogram for a carriage the size and formation of the panel upon which the ornament is intended to be used must be reckoned with. Any other details of general construction, as applied to the vehicle, require consideration in order that the design may have an especial adaptation to its surroundings. The style of the design ought, properly, to be in strict harmony with the style of the vehicle, just as in color the design should harmonize with the colors employed in painting the carriage.

M. W. & CO.

In preparing the design for a surface two methods are given for the transference of the design from the paper to the surface. The design being drawn on the paper, and all inter-lacings clearly denoted by extra emphasized black lines, chalk or whiting is rubbed on the back of the paper, after which it is placed upon the panel and held carefully in position while the lines of the design are gone over with a

hard pencil. By the second method the design, after being drawn, is perforated along its lines with a needle. It is then laid upon the panel and with a pounce of whiting, in case of a dark ground, and charcoal, in case of a light one, the small dots outlining the design are left upon the surface.

Occasionally the workman will wish to paint the monogram upon paper in such a way that it can be used as a transfer ornament. This plan is recom-

L. J. F.

mended when monograms are called for upon vehicles so constantly used that they cannot be taken from service long enough to admit of painting the monograms in the usual way. Take first grade lithograph paper and upon one side apply successive coatings of mucilage until a firm gloss is established. Then outline and paint the monogram upon the gloss side of the paper, using colors and effects that would be appropriate if the painting were being executed upon the panel direct. The unused portion of the paper is now cut off and moistened and the monogram, face down, is pressed solidly upon it and maintained in that position until dry. The monogram is now, both back and face, perfectly sealed between the mucilage clad paper. The paper at the back of the ornament is next dampened little by little until it is sufficiently saturated to permit being lifted easily. This pro- cess completes and fin- ishes the shop prepared transfer monogram, and

M. C. H.

if deftly prepared it should render satisfactory results.

To perform good work in painting monograms due attention must be given the tools. These should consist of mahl stick, palette, palette cups, a small palette knife, pounce bags, small bottles containing japan, turpentine, etc., and a complete assortment of pencils. The pencils should be red sable hair, set in metal, and outfitted with cedar handles. The hair had best not exceed ¼ inch in length, and in size the pencils may run from knitting-needle bulk to what pencil makers call No. 2. As a rule, a pencil somewhat smaller than the No. 1 pencil of commerce will be needed. In the way of pigments the workman should provide himself with an array of the best tube colors. A finely prepared color is a great aid to the workman—

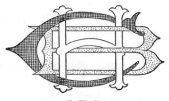

C. H. B.

an aid, let me say, too rarely appreciated. The most popular monogram colors are various shades of greens, and reds having close relationship to vermilion and carmine. In addition, such pigments as silver or flake white, drop black, ultramarine blue, verdigris, burnt umber, burnt sienna, orange chrome, Indian red, chrome yellow and Tuscan red are used.

O. D. T.

The initial of the surname, invariably to be made more prominent than the letters of the Christian name, will submit to strong color effects without offending the visual sense. Perhaps it may be timely here to say that, after recognizing the fact that the striping of the running parts rigidly govern the color or colors of the monogram, there are no arbitrary laws to restrict the color schemes employed. In this as in other branches of ornamental painting the harmony by analogy and the harmony by contrast are recognized and adhered to. The monogram painted in relief is an illustration of harmony by analogy. Such a monogram represents the employment of a single color and its blended tints and shades. Harmony by contrast consists of painting each letter of the monogram a different, but complementary, color. The relief monogram is best done by first laying the design in a medium shade of the selected color. Then the shades proper of the mono- gram are cast in with the dark shades of the color, and the light ones with tints of the color. The vital principle involved in shading is, in the words of an authority, "to shade the under parts of the letter or object lapping it and the opposite side on which the light falls—the shade of the overlapped letter would naturally fall on the under-lapped letter, giving the former a raised appearance."

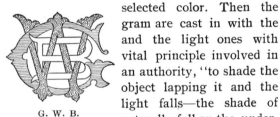

G. W. B.

It has been said that the striping should govern the color or colors of the monogram, as for example: If the gear be striped with carmine the predominating color of the monogram should be carmine; if with orange, then orange; if with green, then green, etc. Granting this, it may also be conceded that the style and general conformation of the monogram should in no small degree compel color effects especially adapted to it. The symmetrical monogram calls for a precisely balanced color scheme, while the clumsy and uncouth one, made so from necessity—and what an inexorable task-master necessity is! —needs a color adjustment that seeks to balance the light parts with the heavy ones, and the heavy with the light.

A. M. N.

Gold and aluminum have of late been largely used in connection with colors and no departure from the correct color principles has thus far been remarked, vehicle users being especially delighted, as well they may be, with the innovation. A practice that has seemed to please the public immensely permits laying the entire monogram with gold or aluminum, as the painter may elect, and then glazing the first letter, say, with ultramarine blue, the next with verdigris, and still the next with carmine.

L. V. R.

If done in gold or aluminum apply a coat of rubbing varnish over the leaf before shading and washing with the transparent colors. Thus will the varnish check the subsequent coatings from striking in and tarnishing the brilliancy of the leaf. In the case of gold being used, follow the varnish with shadings of asphaltum diluted with varnish. The dark shades may be produced by recoating with the asphaltum until the desired shade is reached. Once the asphaltum is quite dry, proceed to coat those parts of the monogram desired to be in colors with such glazing colors as carmine, ultramarine, or cobalt blue, verdigris, etc. The shades of asphaltum are reflected through these transparent colors to the measure of a beautiful appearance, and the sum total of effects thus produced are particularly rich and brilliant. The letters of a monogram painted vermilion glazed with carmine, and the carmine then being shaded with asphaltum and high lighted with pale canary color afford a splendid effect.

G. F. L.

In executing the script monogram the workman will agree with us that carmine and vermilion mixtures produce the finest color effects. In fact, all lean bodied letters show at their best when done in some of the gorgeous reds now popular. A very fetching monogram, as to color, is made by laying the design in vermilion and then glazing part of it with carmine. Or, if the striping suggests green for the color, lay the design in a shade of green to harmonize nicely with the striping, and glaze a portion of it with verdigris. Heavy bodied letters such as are combined in some of the monograms accompanying this chapter show admirably with the upper halves done in vermilion and the nether parts put in Indian red, or, preferably, flamingo red. The vermilion should be given a light wash of carmine, and the letters then outlined with deep orange. In some of the large cities where the trappings and the suits of fashion are ever in the foreground one may see the monogram having one of its letters tricked out in all the finery of a graded shade. The manner of shading consists of beginning at the top of the letter with the palest shade of a certain color, and then gradually deepening the shade as the painting descends until, when the base of the letter is reached, the very deepest and darkest shade of the color is developed. As for example, the striping indicates the employment of green as one of the prominent colors in the monogram. Begin at the top of the letter with the very palest shade of green

A. L.

then continuing with the various gradations down to the deepest shade.   A graded shade is most successfully accomplished with color containing a binder of raw linseed oil to give the pigment a free working property.   A short stiff pencil, lightly, very lightly, tipped with color works most effectively in blending each shade into the next.   Reds and blues respond splendidly to the attractions of the graded shade.

The high lights are justly important features of a monogram.   Many monogramists contend that a high light is almost invariably improved by the addition of a bit of the color of the letter being executed.   As, for instance, the letter is painted medium shade of green, and the high light goes white.   To the white add a dash of the green, and note the restful, pleasing effect secured thereby.

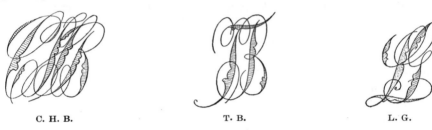

C. H. B.   T. B.   L. G.

High lighting, however, as it applies to nearly all styles of monograms is not suited to the delicate features of the script monogram.   The high lighting of the script ornament should consist in merely flicking those parts needing a relief touch with a color that will denote a slant of light from above.

The provision that permits the striping colors used upon a vehicle to govern, with but few exceptions, the predominating color or colors of the monogram renders a presentation of the color scheme adapted to the accompanying designs superfluous.   Therefore, it only remains for the writer to advise his readers to learn how to design and paint monograms.   It is a buoyant and fascinating art.

CHAPTER XII.

PAINTING THE BUSINESS WAGON: CONSIDERED AS A WORK OF ART
AND AS AN ADVERTISING MEDIUM—VARIOUS PRACTICAL PROCESSES
GIVEN — POPULAR COLOR COMBINATIONS EMPLOYED — PAINTING
CANVAS TOPS, ETC.

ONLY a prophet of much temerity would attempt to bound the possibilities of business wagon painting. It may be allowable to define it as a limitless art, resourceful, restive, responsive to an admirable degree to the ever-varying side-lights of technical skill. All that art can be anywhere the broad surface of the modern business vehicle invitingly offers to display. The time when the main requirement of a business wagon was symmetry and strength of structure has gone by. The merchant, the man of business, has found it to possess a value beyond its mere capacity as a carrier of merchandise. Its worth as an advertising medium, as an agency through which business stability and enterprise may be widely heralded, has been fully learned. Thus the evolution of the present elaborately painted and decorated business wagon has come about. Is it not stating the truth too strongly to say that the average business man is now quite as exacting and peremptory about the style and appearance of his business wagon as he is of his much prized pleasure vehicle. He aims to have his painter achieve a distinct individuality in the painting of his (the business man's) vehicles, so that so-and-so's delivery wagons are readily distinguished from all others met with along the highways and by-ways. To this end he not only seeks to have his vehicles so painted and decorated that unsurpassed advertising effects are commanded, but he also makes careful selection of a combination of colors, and strictly adheres to that combination throughout the list of his business vehicle equipment. This manifestation of exclusiveness on the part of business men has created a spirit of rivalry that has greatly redounded to the painter's benefit in that more beautiful and dashing color effects are now in vastly greater demand than formerly.

And the gratifying aspect of the case is that these original and artistic styles of painting the business vehicle bid fair to continue in popularity. It furnishes the wagon painter, and most especially the apprentice in the wagon paint shop, an incentive to excel in this branch of painting.

The reader may here note, perhaps, an inclination to separate wagon painting, which we have in preceding chapters treated as an inclusive feature of vehicle painting in its broad interpretation, from other branches of the painting art. Necessarily, in the small provincial jobbing paint shop it is all grist that comes to the hopper; consequently carriage and wagon painting are judiciously included under one head. In the city establishment, however, an abrupt division is made, and we find business wagon painting practiced as a specialty—reduced to a fine art. Many argumentative discussions have been conducted by specialists in the two branches to prove the superior skill required in one branch as against the other, and a wide diversity of opinion remains prevalent as to which side has the best of the controversy.

Certain it is, at any rate, that the exactions of fine wagon painting are at present very pronounced. Granting that elegant general effects take precedence over all other features of wagon painting, the fact remains that the quality of the surface must be carefully looked after. It is seldom needful to obtain as fine and satiny a'surface as is required on the panel of the jaunty brougham or the luxurious landau, the color scheme employed, united with dignified and artistic ornamentation, being depended upon as the irresistable attraction. However, this statement is not intended to belittle the importance of the surfacing system. Upon the finest class of business wagons it is a common experience to observe surfaces which in point of smoothness and general excellence are second only to those observable upon heavy pleasure carriages of the finest class.

The wagon painter is confronted by many difficulties concerning which the carriage painter pure and simple, knows little. He must know well how to build beautiful and durable surfaces. He should be a first-class colorist, understanding all the features of color mixing and fully conversant with the laws of harmony and contrast. He will likewise find it necessary to be an unexcelled master of the varnish brush, a skilled striper, wagon letterer, and decorative painter of established ability. The chief disadvantage under which the wagon painter labors is presented to him through the agency of the many lead-weighted colors which he is usually compelled to employ. Many of the light colors extensively used in wagon painting at this time contain keg lead, or lead of another form, as the main ingredient. In doing jobs with light colors containing much lead, roughstuff is not generally used, the lead medium being relied upon to furnish a sufficiently smooth, compact, and close-textured surface; and naturally, therefore, this surface is freely flexible and elastic. Amid the stress and strife of competition and swift processes, these coats are often crowded on so fast that reliable drying is not assured, and then to lend additional uncertainty to the outcome of the work, rather quick and fairly unelastic varnish coats are employed, so that at the completion of the work a thread of weakness gleams through the whole paint and varnish structure. Surface building fallacies of this nature the wagon painter is forced to contend with, and his ability to surmount them is repeatedly shackled by rigid contrary decisions coming from the business office. By this token, then, it is plain beyond the need of further demonstration, that wagon painting is an art that bespeaks for its successful practice technical knowledge and skill of a high order. Its varied phases, none of which are uninteresting and most of which are really fascinating, invite study, and the cultivation of talents, both artistic and mechanical, not required in any other recognized branch of painting. Probably the

PAINTING OF A FULL-PANELED TOP BUSINESS WAGON

offers more difficulties than any other style of wagon. The workman first proceeds to clean off all the grease smears, and then takes full care to get the job thoroughly sandpapered. Then prime job throughout, running parts and body inside and out, top, bottom, etc. If the job is to be painted in dark colors use the priming formula No. 1, given in Chapter III. of this series, and if light colors are desired prime with white (keg) lead thinned to working consistency with raw linseed oil, tempered as to drying with a teaspoonful of japan to each pint of the primer. If no time limit intervenes omit the japan. The running parts, in due time, are next given careful sandpapering, and then rub lead, as fully detailed in Chapter III., is applied. The body receives sandpapering and a lead coat adapted to the final color, mixed, if the job is to go roughstuffed, with $\frac{3}{8}$ oil to $\frac{5}{8}$ turpentine, half and half. Apply to inside as well as outside of body and top, then when these applied mixtures are dry, putty, using as mixture ingredients dry white lead, 3 parts; keg lead, 1 part; and rubbing varnish and japan, equal parts.

For the running parts, if to be painted in light colors, use the next coat of pigment mixed to a brushing consistency with a trifle less than $\frac{3}{8}$ oil and a corresponding increase over $\frac{5}{8}$ turpentine. Thus gradually reduce the percentage of oil as the final color is approached. In case dark colors are to prevail, apply over the red lead a coat of lead pigment carrying a firm binder of oil, say one-sixteenth.

Upon the body, if it is to be painted in dark colors, next apply four coats of roughstuff, choosing from among the formulas given in Chapter III. one suited to the time allowance to be reckoned with. If light colors are to be used, and stuff coats tabooed, all the open, coarse-grained sweeps of the surface require an application of knifing lead (again refer to Chapter III.) put on with a bristle brush and then pressed into the minute wood orifices with a broad blade putty knife. Then in the next coat of pigment, colored fittingly to meet the final color, reduce the oil to the proportion of one-fourth oil to three-fourths turpentine. In the next coat which will have practically a full percentage of the desired color the quantity of oil used, as compared to that contained in the preceding coat, should be cut in twain. The next reduction should bring the pigment down to possessing simply a good binder of oil. Then, in easy procession, follow the final color coat, color-and-varnish, if the system permits it, clear rubbing, and finishing.

On large top paneled jobs, however, when strictly high class results are desired, it will be quite necessary, regardless of the colors employed, to employ roughstuff as the body surfacing agent. The surface is brought up to the roughstuff stage as above advised, and then, in case of a white job, resort is had to the white roughstuff, formulas for mixing which will be found in Chapter V. of this work. The colors used over the stuff coats are either japan ground or washed with benzine to free them as much as possible of the oil carried.

THE CHEAPER CLASS WAGON

is painted by various processes in all of which the several knifing-in pigments are esteemed factors. A moderate cost method affording very neat surface results upon small paneled bodies, ribbed ones, etc., is executed by first giving the body a coat of some P. W. F., the filler being applied freely and at the proper time removed and the surface dried and cleaned up nicely with clean rags. The chamfers on ribbed bodies are gone over with the filler. The day following, the surface is given an application of knifing-in lead, the chamfers getting the same treatment as the flat surface. This knifing-in lead receives a very clean and smooth knifing, the labor of sandpapering being thus reduced to the minimum. This coat having dried, the nail holes and other indentations are next puttied. Sandpapering, first with No. ½ paper, lastly with No. 0, follows. This is made to suffice for a base to color upon, if a light color is desired. If a dark color is wished, a coat of lead, colored to a full slate color and mixed to dry "dead" or gloss free, is put on with a camel's-hair brush. This effectually dresses over and obliterates surface irregularities which might command attention upon dark surfaces, whereas upon light colored ones, built with a strong percentage of lead, they would pass unheeded.

The running parts get a primer consisting of lead, 2 parts; yellow ochre, 1 part; floated in raw linseed oil. The outer or more exposed parts are next draw-puttied with the regulation knifing lead, this to be followed in due course with regular carriage putty, being smoothly placed in nail holes and other cavities. Sandpapering next ensues and this, in turn, is followed with a gloss-lacking lead coat in which the final color is well represented.

Perhaps a still cheaper system, as practiced in a factory shop, may be wanted. If so, prime job throughout, body and gear, with a pigment strongly colored with the color to be used in painting the vehicle. This primer, for its liquid ingredients, should have raw linseed oil, ¾; turpentine, ¼; japan, 1 teaspoonful to each quart of the mixture. Stand the work aside in a warm room for at least 48 hours. Then thoroughly sandpaper with No. 1 paper, after which putty holes, etc. Now take the body surface and give it a coat of knifing lead made of dry white lead, ⅝; keg lead, ¼; finely ground roughstuff filler, ⅛; rubbing varnish, ½; japan, ¼; turpentine, ¼; color this lead to meet final color. Exercise great care in cleaning off all surplus lead so that a very light polish with No. ½ sandpaper will suffice to insure adequate surface smoothness. This knifing lead will require thirty-six hours in which to dry reliably. Then reduce the consistency of quick rubbing varnish somewhat with turpentine, and apply a coat to the surface. With clean linen cloths wipe off the surface immediately. This varnish coat serves to act as a stopper and sealer-up of the knifing lead and putty, in addition to holding forth the subsequent color and varnish coats becomingly. One day after putting on this varnish coat rub the surface lightly with No. 0 sandpaper to flick off dirt atoms, etc., dust carefully, and lay the first coat of color, a strong binder of varnish being used in both the first and second coats of color. From this out, color, ornament, and finish in the usual way.

The running parts are draw-puttied on the priming coat, puttied, sandpapered in good shape, colored, and from thence out carried rapidly to a finish. This method affords a pretty acceptable finish, especially if tricked out with a neat turn of ornamentation and a fine show of varnish.

Again the practice is observed in some establishments of painting the running parts as just described and doing the body as follows: After priming as usual, a coat of roughstuff mixed of lead and filler, equal parts by weight, and rubbing varnish and japan, equal parts, thinning to an easy brushing consistency with turpentine, is applied. After giving this coat twenty-four hours to dry, sandpaper with No. $\frac{1}{2}$ paper to clear off lumpy substances, etc. Clean off surface carefully and draw-putty with a mixture composed of dry white lead, $\frac{2}{3}$; keg lead $1\frac{1}{3}$; liquids, rubbing varnish $\frac{2}{3}$; japan, $\frac{1}{3}$. This coat can be worked over in ten hours if necessary. Then apply two coats of roughstuff mixed as above suggested, the two coats being applied in one day if the limitations of time so demand. If it is wished to avoid the use of a guide coat, and at the same time enjoy whatever advantages are afforded by such a coat, give the last coat of roughstuff a strong dash of yellow ochre.

PAINTING HEAVY TRUCKS AND FARM WAGONS.

At present this class of vehicles is painted in a way differing considerably from that practiced formerly. Then durability was the chiefly considered virtue. Now that fickle and flighty feature of painting is an attainment no more earnestly worked for than is a high degree of excellence in color effects.

For trucks, while a wide range of colors are popular, radiant reds and yellows are apparently in the greatest favor. The wheels of such vehicles are best given a coat of raw linseed oil before the tires are set. The remaining running parts and the body parts are likewise coated with oil before the irons are fitted, whenever it is possible so to do. It is then easier to clean off grease daubs and finger marks left by the athletic blacksmith and his coy young assistant. Moreover, there is a saving of time gained by this method. The next coat should be a half-oil, half-turpentine lead coat tinted or shaded stoutly with the color to be used in painting the vehicle, unless the color is to be a yellow, in which case a pure white will be an entirely correct ground. If a better job is desired apply an extra coat of lead and an additional coat of rubbing varnish. Beautiful canary yellows are now seen on a great number

of city truck running parts. These yellows can be purchased of the manufacturers ready for use, barring a simple thinning down with turps and the
addition of a little varnish for a binder. Upon the first coat of lead, puttying
should occur. If red or some equally positive color is to be used, color putty
accordingly. If yellow, let the putty go white. Sandpaper and smooth
surface down finely upon the first, and, if used, the second coat of lead. In
using light colors, the mechanic will find it needful to keep clean hands, as
the slightest smear makes a disfigurement not easily remedied. For first-
class, solid jobs of canary or other delicate yellow, two coats of the flat color,
and one coat of color-and-varnish will quite surely be required. The varnish
coats when used clear should be very pale, in fact, colorless. Happily, it is
now a comparatively easy matter to obtain varnishes specially adapted to
light, sensitive yellow and white surfaces.

Many of my readers located in the provincial jobbing paint shop will
have more or less of farm wagon painting to do. As a possible means of
aiding them somewhat in getting the job ready for the color stage of the
process, it may be said that when the job arrives at the paint shop, the first
and most important thing is to prepare the surface for the first coat of oil and
pigment. When possible it is advisable, as in case of heavy trucks, to coat
the job, prior to fitting the irons with raw linseed oil. If anything, the average country blacksmith is given to a more lavish surface adornment of soot
smears, valve oil chromos, and scorched quarter-sections than his city brother
of hammer and tongs. Such surface defacements are all violent enemies of
durability. Their sleek and clean removal is therefore imperative. To
banish the oil and grease and soot smears, saturate a cloth in benzine and
lightly wash the surface. This fluid will loosen and quickly remove, with
the aid of a clean cloth for a final drying up, all the greasy substances. The
scorched patches require a very thorough cleaning out, a piece of glass nicely
answering, usually, for slicking off the carved wood. When the parts are
freed from the burnt particles, touch them lightly with raw linseed oil, wipe
dry with a bit of cloth, subsequently touching the places with shellac. The
priming coat, or first pigment coat, rather, should be controlled by whatever
color the job is to be painted. Putty on this coat. Then a lead coat still more
heavily fortified with the final color is in order. A coat of color-and-varnish
should suffice for a suitable base to stripe and finish upon, save in case an
extra color coat and an extra varnish coat will be needed.

Farm wagon bodies may get priming, a coat of knifing lead, a very
smooth sandpapering on this coat, then a coat of color, one of color-and-
varnish, then finishing varnish. If a little better surface is wished, a coat of
clear rubbing varnish, surfaced closely, will give the desired result. Dark
rich browns for the bodies harmonize effectively with almost any of the
popular yellows for running parts. Indian red, five parts; Prussian blue, one
part; with a dash of yellow to tone the mixture, give a beautiful brown.
Chocolate, maroon, and wine color, also furnish strikingly handsome results

for farm wagon bodies, when shown over running parts attired in gay coats of yellow.

COLORS FOR BUSINESS WAGONS.

As already suggested, a wide variety of colors of striking brilliancy are being used in painting business wagons. Perhaps the prevailing colors may be referred to as the various shades of yellow, reds, and greens. Chocolates, maroons, browns, and rich shades of blue are also extensively employed. Many light delivery wagons are painted solidly throughout, body and running parts, with some one of the beautiful shades of canary yellow. The lettering and ornamental work upon the body may be done in aluminum leaf, the shadings and striping being placed in green or blue. A full-paneled top business wagon may be painted in this way and the color effects will be handsome. The main body panel, lower and front panel, rich wine color; center panel, moldings and other spaces, medium carmine; inside edge of moldings go black, striping white. Letter in gold and shade in blue, light and dark. Running parts, carmine; striped $\frac{1}{4}$ inch black line, and fine line of white. Or the body panels may be done in deep ultramarine blue, moldings black, with letters in gold and ornaments and striping in gold and white. Running parts, light ultramarine blue striped two round lines of white, five-sixteenths of an inch apart. Again the main panel of body may go sage green or a fine cream yellow. If sage green, paint lower panels merrimac green; running parts still lighter shade of green. Lettering done in fine gold outline, striping and ornamenting done in gold. In case main panel is done in cream yellow, throw lower panels in carmine. Letter in gold. Running parts go a lighter tint of cream, and stripe black to correspond with black moldings on body. The fine line should be carmine. If desired, paint body and running parts carmine, letter in gold or aluminum, and stripe with vermilion. Moldings on body, black. Another combination shows the upper panel black, lower panels and running parts, cherry red; or upper panel black, lower panels amber brown, or deep green, with belt panel olive green; running parts, a trifle lighter green. The upper and lower body panel, in case of a three-panel job, may go Indian red, center panel white; running parts Indian or Tuscan red. Letters and striping done in gold and white.

A popular style of painting the ribbed body wagon is to paint body panels dark, rich green; chambers, black; running parts, vermilion. Panels of body striped primrose or orange yellow; running parts, black.

However, to mention in detail a very small part of the charming color schemes which are sought and displayed in painting the modern business vehicle would reach beyond the alloted limit of this chapter. Suffice it to say that the painter has a richly blossoming and variegated field of colors from which to select those combinations sanctioned by the esteemed and appropriate standard of the colorist's art.

PAINTING CANVAS AND CLOTH TOPS.

Formula No. 1.—Use of white vitriol one-quarter lb. in three quarts of soft water, adding whiting until a good spreading consistency is reached. Prime outside of top and curtains. This leaves the material nicely flexible and coats the texture up so dense and full that a couple of coats of paint are saved. Then with an elastic paint coat and finish in the usual way.

Formula No. 2.—Coat the canvas, barring curtains, with rye flour paste, inside and out. Permit this paste to dry thoroughly. With No. ½ sandpaper polish cloth lightly to knock off nibs, etc. Then coat with white lead paint mixed with one-third raw linseed oil and two-thirds coach japan, the mixture cut a little with turpentine. Next coat reduce the oil to a trifle less than one-quarter oil to one-half japan, one-quarter rubbing varnish, the remainder, turpentine. Next give coat white color-and-varnish. Rub this coat lightly with water and pumice stone (pulverized), letter, ornament, and finish with a durable finishing varnish.

Formula No. 3.—Size with hot glue water, using two coats twenty-four hours apart. Then apply coat of keg white lead mixed two-thirds raw linseed oil, the remaining one-third being japan and turpentine, equal parts. After five days apply coat of lead containing three-eighths oil, two-eighths japan, three-eighths turpentine. Then apply white color-and-varnish. Rub lightly, letter, and finish. This is not adopted to a limited time allowance.

Formula No. 4.—Sponge with water top and side panels or curtains; permit to partly dry and then coat with lead and oil coloring strongly in the direction the final color is to be. Reduce the quantity of oil in the next coat, and in lettering use enough oil in the colors employed to give the requisite elasticity.

To paint on enameled drill, mix the pigment with raw linseed oil and gold size japan, equal parts, and thin to the proper consistency with turpentine. In judging the quantity of oil used, a close determination of the percentage of oil contained in the lead should be made, otherwise an excessive quantity of oil is apt to be used.

The wagon painter frequently has to letter on canvas, duck, or some other material of similar texture not dressed in the raiment of paint. To do this successfully various expedients are resorted to. Some workmen practice moistening the cloth with water and then putting on the letters in paint having plenty of oil in it. Others draw the cloth tight and firm and size it with a solution of starch and water. Proportions, ¾ water; ¼ starch. Allow this size to dry considerably before beginning to letter. Mix the lettering pigment to a paste form in elastic rubbing varnish and thin with turpentine. Still others make a size of cooked starch and glue water, and sponge the parts that are to be lettered. After the letters have been placed, if the cloth should prove to be stiff and inelastic, sponge with moderately warm water, in this way abstracting the surplus size.

CHAPTER XIII.

VEHICLE REPAINTING: HOW THE VARIOUS CLASSES OF WORK ARE
DONE—MATCHING COLORS—BURNING OFF PAINT—MATERIALS USED
IN PAINTING—TREATMENT OF TOPS AND DASHES—WASHING FIN-
ISHED WORK—SCHEDULE OF PRICES, ETC.

THE re-varnishing, re-painting, etc., of vehicles constitutes an
important source of revenue for the carriage and wagon painter.
Many first-class paint shops connected with high grade carriage
manufacturing establishments do a heavy business in re-painting vehicles.
The writer has in mind a firm of carriage builders located not far from the
office of THE WESTERN PAINTER, which employs a force of from sixty to
eighty painters. In addition to painting and finishing the manufactured
output of the establishment, consisting, it may be said, of anything in the
carriage line from a tiny road buggy to a dashing four-in-hand coach, the
force is yearly credited with from $30,000 to $40,000 worth of re-painting,
etc. From this it will be assumed that vehicle repainting, rightly directed,
affords substantial profits. Were it otherwise the firm in question would not
make it a part of their business.

TOUCH-UP-AND-VARNISH.

The touch-up-and-varnish job is supposed to reach the paint shop
showing but few evidences of grim-visaged service. The fact that it doesn't
uniformly do so furnishes the painter with about as much difficulty in satisfactorily handling this class of work as he encounters in doing those classes
which have a more troublesome look to them.

The best profits to be gleaned from this class of work are realized when
the room space will admit of locating the job in a position where it can be
handily worked at without much unhanging, and where plenty of light may
be secured. A simple removal of the shafts, wheels, and, if necessary, top,
together with such interior furnishings as carpet, cushion storm apron, etc.,
will, in a majority of cases, suffice to clear the way for active work upon the
job, provided sufficient room space is at command. The unhanging of some
of these "touch ups" is sometimes an expensive item, especially when rusty
bolts are to be taken out and replaced. Therefore, the least possible
unhanging should be practiced. Once the necessary parts are removed, proceed to clean off the grease smears, wiping axle arms bright, and looking
well to the fifth wheel. Benzine is a good, quick liquid agent for loosening

grease, etc. If top is left upon the job (and it should be in most cases, when possible), dust out the lining carefully, clean outside well, then clean out the body interior, after which give the outside body surface a light pumice flour and water rub as the most effective means of ridding it of possible greasy patches, dirt nibs, etc. A close, hard rubbing should be avoided, as upon a majority of surfaces it is prone to disclose checks and fissures, minute or otherwise, which a single coat of varnish will only serve to bring out more clearly, rather than to conceal. The body rubbed and washed thoroughly, the running parts are given a careful rinsing and drying off with the chamois skin.

TOUCHING UP.

Matching colors preparatory to touching up is probably the most difficult process related to this class of work. To match colors successfully one must have a correct eye for colors. To distinguish between closely related tints, shades, hues, and tones, in an accurate and conclusive way, brings into play talents, or a gift—call it what you please—not vouchsafed to the average mortal. This is one important feature of the trade that practice does not make perfect. The colorist does not acquire his skill by practice merely.

If the fading of colors tended in one general way and to something like a uniform degree, the successful matching of colors might be controlled in due time by all painters interested in experimental work. Chemistry and other scientific aids to color-making have wrought mysterious and, to the practical man, undemonstrable factors in carriage colors. As a result, colors fade in all the varying degrees imaginable, and are subject to so many influences that their control, as a rule, is quite beyond the skill and practical knowledge of the painter.

Many of the colors, notably the radiant reds lately so fashionable, are naturally so fugitive that unless extraordinary care is exercised in preparing the groundwork, they quickly fade; and, their original identity once lost, it is a feat beyond the ability of the most masterful colorist or color matcher to restore. To a less extent, perhaps, other colors operate in the same way.

The question, therefore, presents itself:—Is not the best way to match colors to prevent their fading, so far as prevention can be made to apply? One's doctor will affirm that a mound of prevention is worth a mountain of cure.

It is not expected to make this prevention so sweeping and effectual as to merit the title of a cure-all. But preventive measures, diligently practiced, will lessen the fading evil, and thus reduce the work of matching colors to the minimum. The mixing of colors, as already alluded to in these chapters, should, so far as it is within the power of enlightened paint shop knowledge, be made an exact process. Carelessness and guess work are not to be tolerated. Exact measurements of all the ingredients which go into a batch of color or paint are necessary. Then a firm insistence upon hardy, durable grounds, regardless of the hurrying shouts of the populace, is in order. A fugitive red, or any other fugitive color, as a matter of fact, is given a support that will add to its permanency, by adjusting the ground color with such a strong binder of varnish that the color has a "live look" to it—an approach to a faint egg-shell gloss, let us say. The retention of the final color's original purity and strength is in this way made more permanent.

In color matching, however, which, despite our best efforts, must continue to be a part of paint shop practice, it is best to take over to the mixing bench a certain part of the work to be touched up, and, touching a few inches of space with varnish so that it can be seen what the spots and what the color as a whole will look like under a fresh coat of varnish, proceed to gauge the matching color to it. It is a principle adhered to by many skilled workmen in the matching of colors that the touch-up color should contain sufficient varnish to cause it to dry with a stout gloss. A color furnished with a strong varnish gloss will reflect more light than it will absorb, and *vice versa*. And the color which in process of drying absorbs more light than it reflects, will, as a rule, when varnished over, be a different color (or a different shade, hue, or tint of that color) than it looked to be in the mixing pot or on the surface after it had simply dried free from "tack." An absorption of light has effected a chemical or other change in it, and what was judged as a close match proves a wide departure from it. Even with the counteracting agency of varnish, a color is pretty sure to dry out lighter than it appears in the mixing cup, so that close calculation and the exercise of the colorist's art in a fine way is needed to get the desired match.

The touch-up color having been satisfactorily prepared and tested, the felloes and all places on the job worn bare to the wood being, in the meantime, touched with lead and oil, the work of touching first the body and then the running parts is carried along.

Then the dressing of the top, side curtains, and, if need be, the dash, ensues. The interior of the body is next varnished, then the outside surface is flowed, and, finally, the running parts.

Coming next to the touch-up-and-varnish job, and by many painters regarded as belonging to the same class, is the job that gets one coat of color, striping, and one coat of varnish. This job offers an opportunity for deception of which the paint shop graduates in the school of intellectual villainy are quick to take advantage. They solemnly assure the prospective customer that they will *paint* his vehicle for, say, $6, the price asked ordinarily for the color and one coat varnish job. The stranger, caught by the price and the alluring prospect of getting the job *painted*, responds to the "hold up" until the dishonesty of the thing is revealed, as it is sure to be, by the exacting needs of service. The color, stripe, and varnish job calls for no little dexterity in many cases, in placing the color directly over a hard, flinty surface of paint and varnish and making it stay for a reasonable term of service. The surface once cleaned, as per directions in the preceding case, the body is given a light rub with water and pumice stone flour, and the gear is treated to a smart smoothing off with fine sandpaper. These fine, and, to the naked eye, almost invisible scratches and furrows, suffice to afford a foothold, a gripping place, for the color. These hard, adamantine surfaces over which quick colors are often necessarily placed may be classed as prolific sources of color flaking and chipping. In addition to the sandpapering as a means of promoting durability, the use of a strong binder of varnish in the color is advised. The one coat color, stripe, and varnish job is quickly done and should afford a good profit.

The color, color-and-varnish, stripe, and finish job simply means a coat of color-and-varnish applied over the color after it has been placed as just described. Then a "mossing" or rubbing with hair to the extent of knocking of the gloss of the color-and-varnish, striping, and finishing, the body surface, of course, to get a rather light rub with water and pumice stone, both before applying the color and after applying the color-and-varnish. Should the body surface show signs of being fissured and cracked somewhat, it were better to forego the rubbing with pumice stone and water, substituting therefor a dressing down with No. ½ sandpaper. This provides against moisture getting into the checks and causing trouble.

Following in the wake of the above class of work come the jobs that are afflicted with all sorts and conditions of surface ailments; jobs that ought properly to be burned off if the owners could be convinced of the economy of the process. One way of treating a body surface threaded with fissures consists of taking a two-inch scraper, such as car painters use, made of a file cranked over at both ends so as to give two cutting blades, and scraping the varnish completely off down to the undercoatings of color and paint. Follow the scraping with a quick rubbing with lump pumice stone or a fine grade of brick and water, avoiding even a close approach to the wood. In most cases the cracks will, by this process, be pretty cleanly removed; when they are not entirely slicked off the remaining vestiges are, as a rule, so faintly traced as to give no further trouble when bridged over by the coats of lead, color, and varnish. The rubbing once completed, the surface is given time to dry out thoroughly; then sanding with No. 0 ensues, this, in turn, giving way to a coat of facing lead mixed to dry without gloss, the lead being colored to a decided slate shade with lampblack. Apply with a camel's-hair brush. Sandpaper this coat with No. ½ paper; then apply color, and finish out as previously advised in these chapters. If a different plan of filling up is preferred, cut down the surface with No. 2 sandpaper, and first apply a lead coat mixed of ⅓ raw linseed oil to ⅔ turpentine. In 48 hours give a coat of roughstuff made of keg lead and filler, equal parts by weight, thinned to a stiff paste with rubbing varnish and japan, half and half, and then reduced to a free brushing consistency with turpentine. First puttying should be done on the lead coat, and the second one on the first filler coat. A couple more of roughstuff coats will suffice to give the needed body of rubbing pigment. Thus the old flinty foundation is furnished with the requisite elasticity through the medium of the oil lead coat. The roughstuff foundation is made to dry hard and firm, like unto the condition of the old foundation itself, and in this way an affinity between the old and the new is established.

Another foundation is quickly builded by taking any good roughstuff filler and reducing it to a spreading consistency with shellac, the first coat, however, being made a bit thinner in body than the succeeding coats, so that it will more readily penetrate the cracks. Three coats of this preparation usually suffices to yield the necessary foundation free from fissures or other blemishes. The roughstuff filler and shellac make a compound remarkably quick setting; hence, it must be worked very quickly if smoothness of application would be achieved.

Again, it is the practice in some quarters to sandpaper the old surface down as close as possible, giving a stout coat of lead mixed with $\frac{1}{4}$ oil to $\frac{3}{4}$ turpentine, and when this coat has dried for a couple of days, putty all the deep cavities, following, the day after, with a glazing of putty over the surface, the glazing being done with a broad putty knife, and the putty being worked out to a uniform film and as smooth as possible.

In respect to the running parts, all flaky, shelly patches of surface should be scraped. All torn and shredded places require smoothing down nicely with scraper and sandpaper. The old remaining paint should be perfectly solid and secure. The parts cleaned and scoured to the bare wood had best be given a lead coat containing, as one of its liquid ingredients, at least $\frac{1}{3}$ linseed oil. The second coat, applied, like the first, with a camel's-hair brush, may contain merely a binder of oil, avoidance of gloss being a strictly observed rule. Then putty deep holes and indentations, following this with draw puttying all parts in need of such treatment. Upon this lead coat, or a second one if the owner is not averse to paying for it, the finish is reached in the usual way, as advised in a former chapter. In painting over these cracked, flaky, and insecure foundations, the first principle to be observed is to get the shaky, shelly material completely removed, leaving nothing but the firm and securely fastened pigment. The second one is to secure as thorough an amalgamation of the old and new materials as practical paint-shop knowledge and skill will insure.

BURNING OFF PAINT.

However good the crack-filling formulas may be, they are at best only expedients of temporary value. Burning off the paint, thus getting a sure foundation from the wood itself, is effective and free from those injurious effects which are so often characteristic of paint removing preparations, etc. As in the past affirmed by the writer, "with the old more or less shaky foundation, concerning the exact nature of which no man knoweth, fairly and cleanly removed, the painter is enabled to work from the foundation coat to the finish with the bright light of knowledge concerning the preparation and application of the materials used, drying, action, etc., flashing through his mind.'' This is why burning off is so much more satisfactory, usually, to the painter. In the lingo of the street, he knows ''where he is at,'' and the measure of security afforded him.

To do first-class paint burning—and the other kind is not to be considered in these chapters—the workman must be provided with a strictly reliable and good-working lamp, burning gasoline or naphtha. To be maintained in a condition to render satisfactory results, the flues and mechanism require thorough cleaning and inspection before the lamp is laid away after use. No unused fluid should be allowed to remain in the reservoir of the lamp when it is not in use, as the vapor arising therefrom will very shortly deposit a film of sticky substance on the surface of the flues that will prevent a smooth and even 'flame when the lamp is again put into use. And eventually, if the flues are permitted to become more or less choked up in this way, the lamp will refuse to work at all. Explosions and accidents of many kinds are possible with the lamp that is allowed to clog and gum up. The burning lamp should be kept in a clean place, and show a clean, bright surface, both interior and exterior. A couple of putty knives, one narrow and one broad blade, a good, serviceable glove or mitten provided with a wrist and half-arm sleeve, and a leather apron reaching well up to the workman's chest, belong to the burner's kit, and should be kept in close company with the lamp.

The operation of burning consists in simply directing the flame upon the surface long enough to soften up the pigment and permit of its easy removal with the knife. In a way, ''burning off'' is a misnomer. To literally burn the paint off, as the apprentice might possibly construe the term if not otherwise enlightened, would result in charring the wood to a harmful extent. Begin burning at a part of the surface which will allow the softened paint to be thrown off over a portion of the surface still coated with paint. As the knife is usually handled with the right hand it is best to begin burning on the left side of the panel. Thus the softened paint is thrown to the right and across the unburned portion of the surface. It is a wise rule to remember, in connection with this work, that a job burned right is in a fair way to be painted right. If through an accident or otherwise the surface should get scorched in places, a complete scraping out of the burned wood fibres will be necessary. Then with equal parts of raw linseed oil and turpentine touch just the charred patches. After a solid block sandpapering, the surface may be taken in hand and conducted to a finish in the usual way.

TABLE OF MATERIALS USED IN PAINTING VEHICLES.

For a landau:—

BODY.

Priming	2 quarts
Lead	1½ "

Putty ....¾ to 1½ lbs.
Sandpaper............ .... 10 sheets
Roughstuff (four coats)................................ 1 gallon
Guide coat... ¾ quart
Color (per coat)....................................... 1 pint
Color-and-varnish (2 coats)........................... 1½ quarts
Clear rubbing (1 coat)................................ 1½ pints
Coat of finishing...................................... 1¾ "

RUNNING PARTS.

Priming.........................,........................ 1⅛ quarts
Rub lead.. 1¼ "
Lead coat... 1 "
Putty... ½ lb.
Sandpaper.. 12 sheets
Color .... 1 pint
Color-and-varnish (per coat)........................... 1½ pints
Clear rubbing.. 1½ "
Coat finishing... 1 quart

In the case of a Berlin coach, perhaps the quantity of each item of material should be increased over the above to the extent of ¼ for the body surface. Running parts require the same quantity. The body of a six-passenger rockaway will need, approximately, ⅛ less material than the body of the landau or couch. The body of the coupe-rockaway ¼ less. Running parts consume about the same quantity as the heavier vehicles here named.

The quantity of varnish named for the above vehicles provides for toe-boards, checks, steps, bottoms, etc.

For buggies of the various styles:

BODY.

Priming.. ⅝ pint
Lead .... ½ "
Putty... ¼ lb.
Sandpaper.. 6 sheets
Roughstuff (4 coats)................................... 1 quart
Color (2 coats).. 1 pint
Lampblack (for bottoms)................................ ½ "
Color-and-varnish...................................... ⅝ "
Clear rubbing (2 coats)................................ 1 "
Finishing varnish...................................... ⅔ "
Varnish in color and filler............................ 1 "

RUNNING PARTS.

Priming... 1 pint
Lead (2 coats)... 1¾ "
Putty... ⅜ lb.
Sandpaper.. 12 sheets
Color .... 1 pint
Color-and-varnish...................................... 1¼ "
Clear rubbing.. 1¼ "
Coat of finishing...................................... 1½ "

Such light pleasure vehicles as surreys, cabriolets, etc., require an increase in the quantity of each item of material over that accorded to the buggies and phaetons of about one-half.

The above tables may be of benefit to some of my readers who desire a practical basis upon which to estimate the cost of the material to be used upon a certain vehicle. Labor is said by competent authorities to represent 75 per cent of the cost of painting a vehicle. With the cost of material at hand—a computation made comparatively easy by the aid of the tables here set forth—and with 75 per cent of the whole cost credited to the labor item, a very close estimate upon general vehicle painting can be made.

Guess work in gauging the price of a job of vehicle painting paves the way to an unprofitable business venture; more surely in' these days of up-roarious competition than in times past. Careful estimates, which include cost of labor, material, shop rent, wear and tear of tools, and such other incidental features of business which may properly be taken note of in an estimate, have come to be imperative necessities in carriage and wagon painting. Verily, it is true that it is not all of painting to paint—*estimating* should be included therein.

TOPS AND DASHES.

The proper care and treatment of carriage tops and dashes forms one of the significant features of the re-painting business. About every class of citizens who have to do with carriages—the trimmer, harness-maker, livery man, blacksmith, hack-driver, and jockey—regularly come forward bubbling over with advice and formulas for the preservation of tops; but usually the paint shop is resorted to as the Court of Appeal. The aim of the painter should be to impart to the top and dash a finish which will correspond to that given the other parts of the vehicle, at the same time furnishing the leather or rubber a preservative agent that will provide reasonable durability.

In every jobbing paint shop a space should be set apart for the safe and clean storage of tops and dashes; also cushions, carpets, and other interior furnishings. In the space selected for the purpose a rack made to conform to the size of the space may be erected. Build it to consist of two tiers, with a half-story tier above for the holding of cushions, carpets, etc. If the space is large enough, make the rack, say, 12 feet long, 10 feet high, and 4 feet wide. The two first tiers will hold six buggy tops. The rack is made of 1-inch and 2-inch stuff, hemlock, say, and need not cost to exceed $1.50. Tops that are regularly calashed will require only half space. Under no circumstances should a top be calashed and stored away in the shop unless it has been used and subject to such treatment. The top (and the dash also, when removed), upon removal should be cleaned thoroughly before being set away. If the top joints need a coating of lead it should be given them prior to placing them in the rack or permanent storage place. It is bad policy to defer painting and finishing such parts until it is nearly time to hang off the other parts of the vehicle. A uniform quality of finish cannot in this way be secured. The irons on tops, if chipped, rusted, etc., require lead, often a facing with putty, color, color-and-varnish, a light rub with pumice stone flour and water, and finishing with a good hard drying varnish. A few days before the vehicle is finished the top belonging to it may be taken in hand, the lining carefully dusted out, and the leather or rubber sponged off and dried over with a chamois skin. The further treatment may depend upon the material of which the top is composed. A great many vehicle owners, livery men in particular, prefer to have leather tops—except the badly worn ones— go without a dressing of any kind, a simple washing with castile soap and soft water being thought to amply suffice. Hand-buffed leather tops in good condition, in the writer's estimation, require no dressing; the machine-buffed ones, however, are benefited by a thin, evenly-applied coat of some strictly reliable enamel top dressing. And it is pertinent here to say that even the best of dressings, those which long usage has sanctioned as of established value, are of such a nature that they are beneficial only when applied sparingly. A dressing, to be genuinely useful to the carriage painter, should preserve the enamel of a top, strengthen the leather or rubber, and enable it to retain its natural flexibility for the longest possible period.

If, then, the top be rubber or machine-buffed leather, apply dressing, not forgetting the side curtains. If a leather top and the owner wishes it to be given some preparation other than the regulation enamel top dressing of commerce, the following formulas may be used, the two first being particularly beneficial to the leather.

Formula No. 1.—Neatsfoot oil, 1 pint, beef suet, ⅛ lb. Melt the oil and suet together. Then add a tablespoonful of melted beeswax, mixing the ingredients carefully, and confining in an air-tight vessel. The beeswax has a cooling property greatly to be desired in a leather preservative.

Formula No. 2.—Darken neatsfoot oil with a drop black. Apply sparingly and rub out well with soft rags. This formula does not give the brilliancy of finish that an enamel dressing does, but it gives to the leather a softness and pliability not obtained otherwise.

Formula No. 3.—Adapted for either rubber or leather. Of finishing varnish, 1 quart; beeswax, 1 oz; drop black, sufficient to color mixture properly. Thin to a brushing consistency with the turpentine. The worth and reliability of No. 3 is vouched for by a jobbing shop painter of twenty-five years' experience.

Formula No. 4.—This provides for the use of boiled linseed oil stained with drop black thinned with turpentine. Apply this preparation with a brush, rubbing it out well and uniformly. Set aside for 30 minutes; then with clean soft rags, rub the mixture off, polishing until a clean cloth shows no stain when rubbed over the leather. Places which show cracks and hard service will need a second coating with the mixture. The leather is not thickened with this mixture, has no unusual attraction for dust and dirt, and will remain soft and flexible.

Fine grained leather dashes, fenders, etc., which do not look worn or rusty, appearing only soiled and somewhat smeary, may be gone over with a cloth saturated lightly with kerosene oil, and then polished with soft woolen rags.

The commoner grades may be given patent enamel dressing, or, if preferred, a thin coat of drop black rubbed off immediately with soft rags and then flowed with a first-class finishing varnish. If much worn, they may be greatly freshened up and renewed if treated with some of the formulas given herewith.

MARKING AND METHODS OF IDENTIFYING VEHICLES AND THEIR PARTS.

The jobbing paint shop requires and should be given a system of marking and tabulating all work taken in, so that when the finish is reached and hanging off occurs, valuable time need not be wasted in searching for mislaid and unidentified parts, such as cushions, carpets, storm aprons, and the like. Unless each part is carefully marked with a properly filled out tag attached to said part, and an itemized entry made in the receiving book fitted with printed forms, a filled out form being given the vehicle owner and a duplicate copy retained by the painter, "confusion worse confounded" may be expected to occasionally occur. The following is a blank form which the writer several years ago published and, having seen it in use in the painting business, he can cheerfully endorse its merits as a practical working form:

RECEIVED FROM ....

BY ....

	DAY	MONTH	DATE
RECEIVED ON.........			
TO BE FINISHED ON...			

ARTICLES LEFT WITH ....

....

....

REMARKS...

....

....

WASHING FINISHED WORK.

The duty of the painter does not end with the hanging off of the finished vehicle. He has still one other important mission to perform, namely, proffering advice to the vehicle owner upon the preservation of carriage surfaces. Such advice may be directed along the following lines:—

Carriages require storage in apartments free from dampness, furnished with plenty of light, invited if possible, from all sides, and entirely removed from the stable and its attendant emanations of ammoniacal gases. Ammonia, make the vehicle user understand, is a deadly enemy to colors and varnish. Brick walls may also correctly be classed as paint and varnish enemies causing loss of lustre and general deterioration A newly-varnished vehicle surface is greatly benefited, once the varnish is sufficiently hard to permit it, by frequent washings with clean cold water. Premature water baths, however, are to be avoided, save when made absolutely necessary by reason of mud spotting or other accidents of that order. The suggestion one hears occasionally offered to the effect that a surface may be safely rinsed with water three days after being finished is not founded upon practical paint-shop or varnish-making philosophy, so long as it is made to apply to a high-grade elastic varnish. Such a varnish may be, to a mere finger touch, quite dry, but in reality only the outer film is partially dry, and putting it into service or submitting it to a cold water bath are each in their turn risky experiments. The fact that an elastic varnish has reached the free-from-dust drying stage should not be taken as a trustworthy indication that the time for washing has arrived.

There is no question concerning the benefit of a cold water rinsing to a varnish surface that has well hardened as to its outer film. Frequent washings will then improve its lustre and durability. It must always be taken into consideration that in the case of first-class painting, assimilation of the various varnish coats ensues, and a fair measure of time is therefore necessary after the aplication of the finishing coat ere the washing can be safely given. In washing a varnish surface, gaseous impurities which so readily accumulate, are removed.

Varnish, when at a certain temperature, is susceptible of contraction when any colder body is brought in contact with it. This is the controlling principle of varnish washing. The contraction of a not properly hardened varnish, after cold water is applied to it, causes the liquid gas of the varnish to escape through the medium of evaporation. Drying, according to the natural laws of drying, a varnish retains those elements which add to its brilliancy and elastic properties. When forced to dry by virtue of premature cold water flooding, unfavorable results may be expected to follow.

Washing a newly-varnished vehicle should never occur under the bright glare of the sun. Plenty of water flooded gently upon the surface with a soft sponge is a necessity in the washing process. Dirt accumulations, if any, are softened and carried from the surface under the volume of water. After a careful sponging, the surface may be dried off nicely with a clean lint-free chamois skin. If a hose be used, it should be adroitly wielded, and the stream so gauged that no harm can come to the surface from the water pressure. The hose in the hands of an incompetent coachman is the cause of a great many accidents to freshly laid varnish.

Caution the washer against wetting the inside of the carriage body. Glue joints, etc., do not strongly resist the attacks of water. Under no circumstances permit water to dry on the surface. Stains more or less pronounced are almost sure to follow. Hot water, soapy water, or water not strictly clean should not be allowed to come in contact with a surface of varnish. Do not allow mud to dry upon the surface. Wash it immediately upon its return to the carriage house after being run in the mud.

SCHEDULE OF PRICES FOR RE-PAINTING.

The prices here given are presented in the nature of a working plan for the benefit of painters located in the smaller towns and villages of the country. The schedule is subject to revision or correction in localities where the prevailing grade of work does not warrant the adoption of the prices herein set forth.

Touch-up and varnish buggy or phaeton (dress top if necessary)...$ 5.50
Rubbing bodies of above jobs, give coat of color throughout
bodies and gears, stripe and finish.. 7.00
Extra coat of varnish to above jobs...................................... 2.00
Burning paint off body of phaeton or buggy, surfacing gears with
lead and re-painting throughout 15.00
Burning paint from gear... 3.00
Touch-up and varnish surrey.. 7.00
Extra coat of varnish for above job....................................... 3.00
Extra coat of varnish for body.. .1.50
Painting surrey throughout... 14.00
Burning paint off entire job and re-painting 20.00
Touch-up and varnish cabriolet.. 10.00
Extra coat of varnish for above job....................................... 4.00
Extra coat of varnish for body.. 2.00
Painting cabriolet first-class throughout................................. 23.00
Burning paint off body...... .... 3.00
Burning paint off job entire and painting................................. 30.00
Touch-up and varnish a four or six passenger rockaway.... .... 20.00
Additional coat of varnish for above job.................................. 10.00
Surfacing upon the old paint structure and re-painting............... 40.00
Burning off body and re-painting job 50.00
Touch-up and varnish brougham or landau.............................. 25.00
Surfacing and painting over the old paint structure.................. 48.00
Burning paint off body, re-painting, and finishing throughout..... 60.00
Touch-up and varnish Berlin coach.. 30.00
Surfacing and painting upon the old paint............................... 55.00
Burning paint off body, re-painting and finishing entire............ 70.00
Painting and finishing hearse... 45.00
Burning paint off body, re-painting, and finishing job entire 55.00
Touch-up and varnish hearse.. 20.00
Platform wagons: surfacing and painting upon old paint structure 12.00
Color, color-and-varnish, stripe, and finish............................ 10.00
Varnish light business wagon... **6.00**

Painting light express or business wagon without top.....10.00 to 12.00
Painting top light express or business wagon........................... 2.00
Painting heavy express or business wagon....................12.00 to 15.00
Painting top heavy express or business wagon....................... 3 00
Lettering on vehicles, per foot, plain paint .... .15 to .20
Lettering, per foot, shaded .... .20 to .25
Lettering, per foot, shaded and ornamented....................... .35 to .40
Lettering, per foot, plain gold .... .45 to .50
Lettering, per foot, shaded .... .60 to .70
Lettering, ornamented gold................................. .80, .90, and 1.00

CHAPTER XIV.

A STUDY OF MATERIALS: WHITE LEAD, ITS PURITY, ETC.—QUALITY OF COLORS IN GENERAL—ADULTERATION PRACTICALLY CONSIDERED—PURITY OF RAW LINSEED OIL—TURPENTINE—TESTING COACH JAPAN—VARNISH.

THE name of a thing should not be accepted for all there is to the thing itself. The carriage painter has very pronounced reasons for bearing this fact in mind when engaged in studying and passing judgment upon the materials he finds it needful to use in his business. Probably the most important pigment which finds its way into the carriage and wagon paint shop is white lead. This pigment has afforded a theme for increasing discussion, its qualities and adaptability having been extensively canvassed. Numerous substitutes have been introduced during the past two decades, but white lead still retains its pre-eminent popularity. Lead compounds and various adulterated brands have given the painter plenty of trouble, and caused him to devote more attention to the quality of his white lead stock than formerly. Because of its soft, pliable, grain-filling property, its established elasticity, density, body, fine working quality, and its merits as a reliable drying pigment, white lead is the filling up and foundation material *par excellence.*

The purity of lead deserves the carriage painter's first consideration. It has been practically determined that a pure lead, endowed with all the virtues which should distinguish pure lead, when mixed and used in combination with other pigments or colors, holds its quality better and is less susceptible of change than a compound or adulterated lead. Moreover, pure white lead, with its soft, fine, elastic texture, has a natural adhesiveness, a surface-filling and leveling-up property, which the impure lead carrying a percentage of gritty, flinty ingredients does not possess. The pure lead works out under the brush more pleasantly and with less brushing than the compound, and it dries with greater uniformity, etc.

At the same time it is well to remember that a strictly pure lead may have a number of features in its make-up decidedly objectionable to the carriage painter. It may be imperfectly washed, or it may be too coarsely ground, etc. In his study of white lead, then, the painter will find it a matter of value to determine the adaptability of the lead to the requirements of his business. After convincing himself of the purity of the lead, it remains for him to test for fineness of grinding. A lead ground fine—impalpably fine, if it please my readers— lightens the labor of sandpapering, strikes into the wood fibres stoutly, and covers the maximum surface space. It has good coloring and covering power when mixed with colors to form tints, and for other important parts which a white lead plays in vehicle painting it is especially adapted.

Nor should a carriage lead be ground in too large a percentage of oil. For coats between priming and color but comparatively little oil is needed, and washing out with benzine or turpentine entails an unnecessary amount of labor. Hence, it should be insisted upon that carriage painters' lead be ground moderately stiff in oil, so that protracted washing-out may be avoided on the one hand, and extended mixing and breaking-up operations shunned on the other. A practical and, at the same time, a conclusive test of fineness is furnished by taking two pieces of plate glass 8x8 inches in size, setting them securely in blocks of wood, and then smearing a couple of small flakes of the lead, rubbing the pieces of glass together. Continue rubbing with a firm, even pressure until a uniform distribution of the pigment and a thorough impact is established. The glasses should then disclose the nature of the grinding. To learn the drying power of the lead, take the palette knife and slick a small quantity over the glass and set aside, noting the time consumed in drying. A lead ground in the proper proportion of oil for carriage work should, as taken from the keg and smeared in a thin film over the glass, dry in twelve hours so that the finger may be passed over it without sticking.

What has here been said in reference to chemical purity or strictly pure as a necessity in the white lead product does not apply to all the pigments so useful to the vehicle painter. For reasons here shown lead extenders and lead compounds should be emphatically objected to. A disavowal of their worth as carriage painting pigments, however, in no wise lessens the significance of the fact, as already pointed out, that a strictly pure lead is very often an expensive, if, indeed, it be not a worthless, lead to buy. Chemically pure is not invariably an accurate gauge of quality. A chemically pure lead that has not fineness to recommend it lacks an essentially vital quality. In respect to the pigments and colors following in the wake of white lead it has been made plain on many a hard-fought field of experiment that the color consumer, the practical painter, the workman far removed from the analytic gentleman of the laboratories, is chiefly concerned in getting a pigment or color adapted to his needs more completely than any other available one. It may not be chemically pure as the chemists would construe the term; but if it responds satisfactorily to a practical test, it is then serving the painter's practical need. As declared by the writer, in an article published some time ago, ''a color or pigment may be pure in the sense that it is not adulterated, and still fall short of being chemically pure. It is the duty of the consumer to avoid buying, under the label 'strictly pure,' an adulterated color. The real color contained in such a product is then costing him considerably more than would a color in a state of purity.'' The chemist and the practical painter do not agree oftentimes upon what may be called adulterants. Once upon a time, as the fairy books say, at a painters' convention the chemist employed to make an analysis of chrome yellow stated in substance that practically everything outside of the chromate of lead should be classed as an adulterant or as a matter out of place. The practical painter who has looked up the subject of chrome yellow manufacture could tell the chemist in this case that he has signally failed to take into consideration the necessary constituents of the different shades of chrome yellow. As, for example, acetate and nitrate of lead, bichromate of potash and bichromate of soda, sulphate of soda, etc, are constituents of a pure chromate of lead. And our friend, the chemist, would tell us that a chromate of lead composed of some of the above ingredients is not a chemically pure article. What the carriage painter, the consumer, will find it of value to ask himself is this: Does a given pigment or color suit the requirements of my business? If in doubt as to the utility of the given pigment or color, then an immediate practical test should be resorted to. It is not the purpose of the writer to belittle the position or the usefulness of the chemist. The value of a chemical analysis in the detection of adulteration and in explaining how a color is made is cheerfully acknowledged; but after the chemist's deduction must follow the practical test. In conducting a practical test the foremost aim of the painter should be to consider the color or pigment to be tested in relation to the object for which it is intended. Shade, brilliancy, working property, durability, etc., are entitled to a careful and chief consideration in a test for quality. And a test for quality, if conducted painstakingly and thoroughly, will disclose the real value of the material to the consumer. When extenders are added to a pigment for the sole purpose of enriching the manufacturer at the expense of the consumer, the practice becomes adulteration, pure and simple. If, however, such extenders are used to, and actually do, increase a pigment's usefulness, fortifying it in a way and to an extent that it needs to be fortified, the painter will not attempt to question its commercial value.

The study of the pigments which the vehicle painter calls to his uses is a feature of business deserving the most rigid attention. Carried on watchfully and with a vigilant regard for details, it cannot well fail to increase paint shop profits.

LIQUID MATERIALS.

In the consumption of liquid materials the vehicle painter has no use for extenders. Unfortunately, however, the thrifty and shifty sons of adulteration, after the manner of Marco Bozzaris, in the Fourth Reader, are struggling, tooth and nail, to adulterate linseed oil and the turpentine product in a way to defy detection.

What the cathode ray is to a certain branch of science, pure raw linseed oil is to carriage and wagon painting. Back in a somewhat indefinite period of the past, linseed oil pre-empted the chief claim in the domain of paint and varnish, and its right to a royal office in that domain has never yet been successfully disputed, notwithstanding the fact that a flood of substitutes and counterfeits have been turned loose upon the market. In the language of another, "Raw linseed oil is the king of the paint realm. There are lots of usurpers in the field but they are short lived. The true homage of the brotherhood of the brush continues to be paid to the old stand-by. It is the gold of the paint shop currency."

In the basic stage of carriage and wagon painting, pure raw linseed oil is conceded to be the life of the pigment. Impure or adulterated linseed oil —the spurious, fraudulent article, if you please—has more to do with the premature decay of paint and varnish than one at first thought might concede. During the process of painting there are numerous complications which, by the harsh reality of scientific analysis, could be directly traced to the insidious effects of an adulterated brand of oil. Investigations conducted by competent experts have shown that the self-assertiveness of adulterated oil is determined, not so much by apparent unfavorable effects upon the under coats, but rather from its resistless attack upon the lustre and durability of the finishing varnish. Some of the oils used to adulterate linseed oil are pronounced by such authorities as Hurst and Terry to be good driers, although, as in the case of rosin oil, they may seemingly dry good upon the surface only to soften up later on. And provided these adulterant oils are not good driers, the people engaged in floating them along the avenues of trade have simply to add a certain proportion of drying japan to O. K. them in this respect.

The vehicle painter's practice of using raw linseed oil insures him somewhat against oil adulteration, as it is much more difficult to adulterate the raw linseed product than the boiled and have the fraud go undetected. A raw linseed oil when fresh and new is of a bright yellowish-green color, and as it grows older it becomes paler in color and perhaps a little brighter. When spread on a surface in a thin film and exposed to a pure dry air it will harden quite solidly in from forty-five to fifty hours. It ranks as reliable drying oil, promptly solidifying when acted upon by peroxide of hydrogen or by subnitrate of mercury. A non-drying oil refuses to show a change of this kind. Combining powerfully with oxygen, it offers, when dry, a stronger resinous character than any other oil.

Probably the chief adulterants of linseed oil should be listed as rosin, mineral, and fish oil; cottonseed oil being looked upon with less favor than formerly, while hempseed oil, owing to its pronounced tendency to change color, is not much in evidence at present.

Rosin oil is strictly an unreliable drier. It toughens the working property of paint and is deficient in all the essentials which should distinguish a good paint oil. Its low flash point, as indicated by Hurst,— 300° to 330° F.—together with its strong rosin odor when heated, would appear to make it an easily-detected adulterant. Deodorizing processes have of late served to fortify this oil, and fish oil as well, against detection by the sense of smell. Fish oil, chiefly the product of the menhaden fishing industry flourishing so vigorously along the Atlantic coast, has naturally an offensively fishy odor, particularly when heated. Its main recommendations as a linseed oil adulterant are tersely summed up by Terry as follows: The rapidity with which it oxidizes, and its good body, render it not unsuitable as a vehicle for paint.

The low cost of mineral oils, including coal oil and petroleum, has caused them to become highly regarded as linseed oil adulterating mediums. Mineral oils more unfavorably affect the drying property of paint than its working and spreading property.

Cottonseed oil belongs to the non-drying class of oils, but since recent processes have made possible the elimination of the pronounced acrid taste, its presence in linseed oil by the sense of taste is not easy to expose.

Hempseed oil is a mean tasting, mean smelling, but good drying oil, and only because of its rapid color changes, wearing finally to a dull brown, is its employment in linseed oil restricted to narrow limits.

In testing for linseed oil adulteration, ammonia is often effectively used, equal parts of the ammonia and oil being employed. Cottonseed oil under the ammonia treatment shows an opaque brown. When it is present in linseed oil the liquid goes to an opaque yellow. Fish oil under the effects of ammonia goes white. Rosin oil will disclose its presence in linseed oil if confined in a bottle, with alcohol added in the proportion of five parts of alcohol to one part of oil, and smartly shaken, the alcohol afterwards being poured off. A clear sugar-of-lead solution is added to the oil, and should rosin oil be an ingredient a cloudy precipitate will manifest itself. A practical and simple test often used in the carriage paint shop consists in taking a couple of test tubes and putting a quantity of linseed oil of known purity in one tube and a quantity of suspected oil in the other, then immersing the tubes in warm water for, say, $\frac{1}{4}$ of an hour, and immediately upon removal from the water pouring the pure oil into the tube of suspected oil. If any impurity exists, different colors will form in layers. And it may be here proper to say, in passing, that in making tests and comparisons of materials, an article of established purity and quality should be used as a standard. Some time ago a well-known paint firm issued a card giving some easy and practical tests for the detection of linseed oil adulterants, and knowing their value to the vehicle painter, the writer herewith appends three tests:

No 1.—Shake equal parts of oil and strong nitric acid in a small white glass vial or bottle, and allow to stand from fifteen minutes to two hours.

	UPPER STRATUM	LOWER STRATUM
Pure Linseed oil	Muddy olive green	Almost colorless
Presence of Fish oil	Decided deep red brown	Deep red or cherry color

No. 2.—Shake with concentrated solution of potash or soda, and then add warm water and shake again. Allow to stand half an hour, and if any petroleum (paraffine oil) is present it will separate from the soap.

No. 3.—Put samples of oil in tubes and place them in a freezing mixture (2 parts ice or snow, 1 part salt). If the oils solidify at 0° or 10° to 13° F., then cottonseed oil is probably present. (Pure linseed oil solidifies at 17° F.)

The hydrometer should be among the possessions of every well-regulated paint shop. It is an inexpensive little instrument, and for testing turpentine it is unsurpassed, while for the detection of cottonseed and mineral oil in linseed oil it is a quick and active agent. First test a brand of linseed oil of absolute purity; and such an oil, bear in mind, should not vary ½ degree from 20° to 60° Fahr. In the case of a 20% addition of mineral oil to linseed oil (the same temperature being maintained in testing both the pure and the suspected samples) the specific gravity will be 1½° less than the pure oil. A 25% addition of cottonseed oil will be 1° lower. Fish oil being of about, if not quite, the same specific gravity as pure linseed oil, the adulterator can beat the hydrometer.

Pure raw linseed oil is so essentially a part of durable carriage and wagon painting that especial attention should constantly be directed to the oil supply.

In respect to his purchases of turpentine the painter should be likewise cautious and investigating. The adulteration of turpentine with headlight oil, or a lower grade of kerosene, and with 112 fire test oil has been, and continues to be, actively carried on. This 112 fire test oil, as employed in small southern distilleries not shadowed by inspectors, shows a list of ingredients closely corresponding to, heavy paraffine oil ⅓; kerosene, ⅓; light oil, ⅓. Thus a gravity is provided which registers about the same as pure turpentine and is therefore very difficult to detect. The naval authorities practice—and it is said, successfully—the old-time test of dropping the suspected turps on a piece of white paper alongside of a pure brand of turps and watching the result. The turps containing the 112 fire test oil will leave, upon evaporation, a faint but decided *greasy* stain. Pure turpentine not too rapidly distilled will leave no spot. The turpentine containing traces of the crude gum due to too rapid distillation will impart a sticky, yellowish-white stain to the paper and this the painter should not confound with the aforementioned *greasy* stain of the adulterated turps. In our Eastern, Middle, Western, and Northwestern cities the practice of kerosene oil injection is the favorite method of cheating the consumer. The sense of smell will sometimes detect the presence of kerosene; the white paper test will sometimes expose it; and again both tests will fail, along with the other usual ones. While so keen an authority as Mr. Geo. B. Heckel, of *Drugs, Oils and Paints*, has acknowledged that the adulterators can cheat the hydrometer to a certain extent, it cannot be done with the same measure of profit and im-

punity as formerly.   Mr. Heckel has publicly advised consumers to insist
on 31° turps, prefacing the advice with the following noteworthy declara-
tion: "If I were a painter I would never accept a gallon of turpentine without sticking a hydrometer into it, and if it registered above $31\frac{1}{2}$° or below
$30\frac{1}{2}$° I would not accept it from the United States Treasury."

What vehicle painter vested with the authority of purchasing the turpentine supply for a painting business, be that business big or little, can
afford to disregard Mr. Heckel's admonition?   To pay turpentine prices for
kerosene oil is a disastrous drain upon the resources of a painting business,
in addition to furnishing the materials used an element of insecurity, a germ
of decay, sure to disturb the durability and comeliness of a painted surface.
For it is, or should be, in fact, clearly understood that the kerosene or fire
test oil adulterants do not evaporate like turpentine when put into a pigment
and spread upon a surface.   They strike into the wood or pierce the nether
coat of pigment, causing, later on, the flaking and peeling of the pigment;
or they retard the drying of colors; and again, they lend a peculiar rough-
ness to the surface, like unto that imparted by benzine when used in a fine
coach color.

The carriage and wagon painter has substantial reasons for being interested in coach japans, for upon their quality and judicious employment the
durability of his work greatly depends. The many and beautiful colors which
he uses almost daily are japan ground, and the pigments and colors shop-
mixed are invariably fortified with the ever-useful coach japan.   The wide
variety of names applied to the drying materials used in the painting business has been the source of annoyance and confusion to the practical mind.
In reality, however, there are but three kinds—coach japan, specially adapted
for colors to be quickly dried and containing no oil; liquid drier (or dryer)
intended for the drying of oil and oil paint; and patent driers purchased in
paste form, effective only when used in conjunction with oil.   The patent
driers are so little used at present that they scarcely merit a notice.

Coach japan, with the merits of which the carriage painter has a right
to be concerned, being chiefly used, as before stated, in colors containing no
oil require, for purposes of protection and as a service-insuring medium,
blanketing under one or more coats of varnish.

It is not to be understood that coach japan will not combine with and
dry oil colors; its power in this capacity, however, is less than that of a
liquid drier, while its gummy nature shows a tendency to cause surface dis-
turbances of the cracking and blistering order—most emphatically so when
strictly exact proportions are not maintained.   Its adaptability, therefore, is
best confined to colors containing no oil.

So much of uncertainty, so much that is injurious and fatal to the durability of colors, is embraced in the employment of japan in excessive
quantities or of an inferior grade that the painter should not be slow in determining, by practical tests, both strength and quality.   And to make such

tests easy, not to mention other convincing reasons, need we invoke the purchaser's attention to the importance of buying only standard makes?

A first-class coach japan, as a rule, will show a color moderately light, and when mixed with oil should manifest no disposition to curdle. Such a japan, too, should, when floated in a thin film over a glass or other strictly non-porous surface, dry firm and without brittleness in four hours. To observe how the japan unites and assimilates with linseed oil, take a pane of window glass, that furnishing a surface non-porous and decidedly free from suction, and attaching a sheet of white paper on one side as a means of better showing the action of the oil and japan, drop on the reverse side of the glass about four drops of raw linseed oil. Then affix, say, a single drop of japan in close proximity to the oil, immediately inclining the glass so that the japan may come in contact with the oil. If the drier promptly unites and takes kindly to a close relationship with the oil without curdling or showing other evidences of disagreement, it will merit the approval of the painter. Another easily-conducted test consists in comparing the japan of unknown quality with one of acknowledged merit, by taking the samples and confining them in bottles containing raw linseed oil, shaking the contents and then standing aside for at least twenty-four hours. The proportions of oil and japan may be in the ratio of 5 parts of oil to 1 part of japan, exactly the same proportions being adhered to in all the samples tested. At the expiration of twenty-four hours one can see which sample mixes best with the oil. The samples then poured in a thin film over a piece of glass and allowed to stand will determine the drying property of each. It will also be useful to learn by observation and comparisons if the japan holds well in solution. A japan that fails to do this is not valuable in carriage and wagon painting. Study should be made as to how and to what extent the japan effects the light and delicate colors at present so extensively used. In point of fact, the painter should not weary in investigating the qualities and characteristics of his coach japans, and what they are capable of doing. To establish their real value will mark an achievement of the first order in the economy of painting.

In regard to varnishes the buyer can find no excuse for putting aside the fact that quality and not price should determine the value of his supply; and, happily, he has it within his power in the active prosecution of his business to demonstrate the good or bad quality of varnish. It may frequently prove an expensive experiment; and herein is disclosed an apparently good and sufficient reason for the painter's disinclination to change from the use of one make of varnish to another. The varnishing stage of painting may be said to be in a critical period at all times, and having established the quality of his varnish supply, the responsible party in the matter is naturally opposed to changing in favor of a make with which he is not practically acquainted. At the same time, a practical test of different strictly reliable makes is the only way of deciding to one's own satisfaction which is the best, and the

most economical to buy.   Any first-class finisher can very soon determine
the working property, brilliancy, depth of lustre, drying quality and general behavior under varying circumstances and conditions of different varnishes. Nevertheless, that primary requisite, durability, is not so easily nor
so promptly established.   This essential quality can be determined only
after protracted trials upon vehicles engaged in active service, the painter
retaining carefully tabulated data bearing upon each make of varnish under
observation, the character of the service to which it is exposed, etc.   Thus,
in due season, may the actual merits of a varnish be defined.

CHAPTER XV.

CUTTER AND SLEIGH PAINTING: DECORATIVE ASPECTS OF THE WORK—
THE VARIOUS PROCESSES OF PAINTING EMPLOYED—THE PREVAIL-
ING COLORS—STRIPING AND SCROLLING—REPAINTING, REVARNISH-
ING, PROFITS TO BE REALIZED, ETC.

CUTTER and sleigh painting are justly esteemed interesting parts of the art of vehicle painting. Coming at a time when the ordinary activities of vehicle painting are practically at a standstill, the cutter and sleigh painting business furnishes a medium for profits gleefully taken advantage of by the average factory and jobbing shop painter.

In one way, it must be confessed, this branch of painting has fallen off in attractiveness. The elaborate decorative effects once so largely in the full favor of fashion have been discarded, and many workmen competent to accomplish such effects have become lost in other pursuits. But in these days the painter should be prepared for any emergency; hence it is best that cutter and sleigh decorative work be given study, and skill to execute such work be kept in hand or acquired by practice. Now and then comes a call for a cutter or sleigh ornamented in the old-fashioned way with elaborate arm pieces, etc. The jobbing shop painter especially is very frequently confronted with opportunities for the practice of decorative painting in a variety of ways, and to fulfill his mission as an important community artisan he should be prepared to do the work. The very low prices paid for cutter and sleigh painting at the present time have proved an effective factor, no doubt, in considerably restricting the limitations of decorative painting. At the same time, there is every reason to believe that the conspicuous absence of fine decorative effects in cutter and sleigh painting is also due, to a large extent, to the inability of the average latter-day workman, located in provincial centres, to fittingly produce them. Upon the modern Portland style cutter elaborate ornamentation would perhaps be out of place; but upon many of the runner vehicles of ancient and honorable vintage, which the beauteous Belle of Fashion has decreed to be the proper thing, a generous measure of decorative work would be appropriate. Swell sleighs of more recent pattern take kindly to lavish ornamentation built upon rather delicate lines.

These conditions, therefore, warrant the painter who deeply desires to command profits and success in cutter and sleigh painting, in cultivating a ready skill and dexterity along the lines of ornamental work.

Surface perfections have grown to be important considerations in the

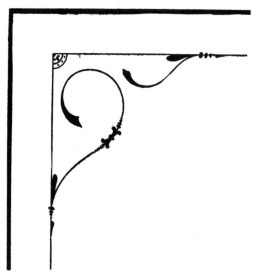

FIG. 1.

economy of sleigh painting of the best grade. While none but the very finest class of cutters and sleighs are given surfaces rivalling in smoothness and quality those reflected by the best class of carriages, still, first-class surfacing remains a chief feature of sleigh painting, excepting at all times the seven-for-$100 vehicles. And in respect to this latter class of jobs, the results achieved in the way of surface effects are often surprising, due chiefly to the very heavy coats of varnish applied. And here the reader may deem it pertinent to ask for a review of the systems and methods practiced in painting and finishing cutters and sleighs.

In the painting of runner vehicles of the best order the jobs are primed throughout, bodies and running parts (and this includes inside of bodies, under surface—everything, in fact, not covered with iron), with oil and lead primer. Permitting this coat to dry thoroughly, a light sanding with, say No. ½ sandpaper, is given, and then a coat of lead containing enough raw linseed oil to bind the pigment securely without giving it a gloss is put on. Use an oval or round bristle brush to apply the lead to the body, and for the running parts use a camel's-hair brush, this latter tool being best adapted to lay a uniform depth of pigment over the sharp edges and small surfaces of the running parts. Upon this coat putty both body and running parts draw-puttying all open-grained portions of the surface. Forty-eight hours after puttying begin rough-stuffing the body, using for the 'stuff equal parts of any good American filler and keg lead, by weight, reducing to a thick paste in equal parts of quick rubbing varnish and japan, then cutting to a brushing consistency with turpentine. This is a two-coat-per-day 'stuff. Apply four coats of the 'stuff, then a guide coat of yellow ochre and set aside for a few days. After rub-

FIG. 2.

bing the surface out (full instructions for rubbing roughstuff may be found in Chapter III. of this series) give it plenty of time—twelve or fourteen hours at least—to dry out. Then lightly sandpaper with No. 0 paper, dust off, and give first coat of color.

The proper color foundation being secured, apply two coats of rubbing varnish, either both clear or one clear and one color-and- varnish, the character of the color foundation determining the selection, and then follow with a heavily flowed on coat

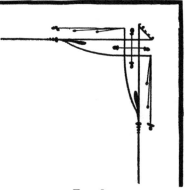

FIG. 3.

of finishing varnish. In case color-and-varnish be used, the striping and ornamental work had best be done on this coat, as upon work of this quality the ornamentation will require the protection of a rubbing, as well as a finishing, coat of varnish.

The running parts require sandpapering, then one coat of color-and-varnish, then striping and finishing. This system, intended exclusively for high class work, requires a very thorough carrying out, with no neglected details from priming coat to finishing, if a satisfactory degree of excellence, both in finish and durability, would be maintained.

Another system, in which roughstuff does not figure, consists of giving body and gear, when received from the wood shop, a coat of lead, ochre, and oil priming. When the irons are attached, the job is sandpapered and a coat of lead containing a durable binder of oil is given. The wood and iron are alike coated with this mixture. The panels of the body are next, in due season, plastered with putty (see Knifing Head Formula No. 1, in Chapter III.),the pigment being firmly forced into the grain of the wood. Aim to get a very smooth application of the pigment in addition to a complete fullness of the wood pores, to the end that the surface cells may be sealed ''against graining out''and that the labor of sandpapering may be reduced to the minimum.

The first coat of color is furnished with a binder of oil and should not be recoated until the day following. Add varnish as a binder for the second

FIG. 4.

coat of color.   A single coat of rubbing, and one of some hard drying finishing varnish often suffices to complete the finish.   If a better job is desired an
extra coat of rubbing is given.   The striping, corner pieces, etc., are done on
the flat color.   The running parts are puttied on the priming coat, exposed
parts of open grained surface draw-puttied, sandpapered, given one coat of
color, coat of color-and-varnish, striped, and finished with a heavy bodied,
hard drying finishing varnish.   Again, for medium priced sleigh work a
factory system consists of applying some reliable liquid wood filler to the job
throughout, then a little later wiping the surface over with soft, clean rags.
The work is allowed twenty-four hours in which to dry out, when the body
is given a coat of roughstuff mixed in the proportion of 3 lbs. of filler to 1 lb.
of keg lead, equal parts of japan and rubbing varnish being used to reduce
it to a heavy paste, and turpentine employed to cut it to the proper working
consistency.   Putty on this coat of 'stuff.   Then apply, at the rate of two
coats per day, a roughstuff made according to the first formula given herewith.   Three coats of this stuff should suffice.   Rub out with rubbing bricks,
color and finish out as previously advised.   The running parts are puttied
upon the filler coat, draw puttied wherever needed, then colored, given color-
and-varnish, striped and finished.

In some shops the roughstuff is discarded altogether, the wood filler being filled over with a couple of lead coats, the first coat containing an oil
binder and the second one containing no oil at all.   This lead foundation is
surfaced down with sandpaper, dusted off, and a wash of quick hard drying
rubbing varnish, thinned down about one-half with turpentine, given.   The
surface is then finished out in the usual way.   The running parts are treated
as described in the liquid wood filler process previously given.

The anti-kalsomine system concerning which considerable discussion
was had somewhat recently amounts to this: The jobs are primed throughout with oil, yellow ochre, and perhaps a little lead.   The bodies are then
taken in hand and all necessary puttying done.   The anti-kalsomine, the
fixer or binder of which is cement, is next mixed to a working consistency
with hot water and applied hot.   It is best to
allow the first coat of kalsomine to stand over
night before being recoated, although in the factory system three or four coats of the cement,
always applied hot, are put on per day.   Then a
liquid mixture of oil, japan, and turpentine, in
the proportion of two parts of oil to three parts of
japan, and one part of turpentine, is flowed over
the kalsomine foundation.   This liquid wash
serves to weld or amalgamate the cement with
the priming coat.   The sandpapering of these
anti-kalsomine foundations is one of the principal
draw-backs to the use of the cement.   It sets in

FIG. 5.

motion flotillas of dust, stifling and suffocating to an extreme. It has been noted, however, that this anti-kalsomine treatment has furnished some fine wearing and very durable surfaces.

The carriage painter in practicing his trade as it applies exclusively to carriages is confined to a comparatively few colors, but in devoting his skill to cutter and sleigh work an extended variety of colors may be used. Artistic instincts are in good demand in the cutter and sleigh painting business. Possibilities for the harmonious combination of colors exist here to an extent not known of in the other branches of painting. Colors sombre and gay; emblematic of this, that, or the other thing; old-fashioned as the days of witch burning or as modern and up-to-date as the '97 color grinder can make them, are all alike acceptable in the sight of the people who love a sleigh ride. Some painters have a great liking for siennas and umbers as body colors for sleigh work. Toned down some they do gleam very showily under varnish. Such colors striped with aluminum or gold and edged with a fine line of red give a strikingly handsome effect, especially if the running parts are painted in some one of the beautiful light reds at present

Fig. 6.

available; or a lighter shade of the body color can be advantageously employed upon the running parts. Perhaps the lighter styles of cutters, speeding cutters, for example, take more kindly to the light and showy reds as running-parts colors than do the vehicles of heavier build, but all styles, nevertheless, permit of brilliant color effects in the treatment of running parts. For a light track or speeding cutter, color the side and back panels medium ultramarine blue; the dash, carmine; running parts, a very light carmine. Stripe the panels, ¼ inch line of gold with a fine line of carmine. The dash and running parts may be displayed with striping of black and gold. Portland cutters for ordinary service show handsomely with the body panels done in ultramarine blue, moldings blacked, with the running parts done in the lightest shades of the ultramarine blue, the job then striped throughout with a primrose yellow stripe. Or again, these cutters are painted deep carmine throughout the body, with light carmine running parts. The striping on body consists of ⅛ inch line of black, and ⅜ inch inside of that is flashed a fine gold line. A Portland amber color for the body, with a lighter shade of the same color for the running-parts, looks fetching, notably so when the body panels are striped with double lines of carmine, the ornamental corner pieces being done in carmine of a lighter shade. The running parts may get a single ⅛ inch line of carmine. Then one can see in the cutter and sleigh centres Portlands done in ashen-grey, canary and lemon yellow, etc.

One of the largest cutter and sleigh factories in this country has this year abandoned the double fine line style of striping so greatly in evidence for several years past, using instead, as a rule, a ⅛-inch carmine stripe—obtained by glazing carmine over a yellow base—with a distance fine line of gold running inside of it. At this establishment one can see a jaunty Portland painted pure white, with the body striped a ⅛-inch blue line with a distance fine line of red. Here also are to be seen beautiful amber browns, charming greens, elegant yellows of the primrose, orange, canary order and extending down to the delicate cream colors. But, on the whole, those cutter and sleigh builders and painters who cater to the worshipers at Fashion's shrine show a determination to adhere to the dark rich colors, such as browns, greens, and blacks, for panel work. Cutters with running parts painted in colors different from those used upon the bodies are not so much in evidence as formerly. Where the dark colors promise to remain in high favor with a large class of the very exclusive folk for some years to come, no strict adherence to such colors may be expected on the part of the general cutter-and-sleigh-using public.

STRIPING, CORNER PIECES, SCROLLS, ETC.

In the striping of cutters and sleighs the real basis of success is a judicious selection of colors. It has been a common saying in factory circles that anything in the way of colors, hit or miss, goes in sleigh painting when the ornamenting is reached. But this should not be so; in point of fact, it is not so in those establishments doing a good class of work. A riotous jumble of colors thrown into a fine line corner piece or scroll is an abominable exhibition of bad taste. There is nothing, we dare say, that so completely stamps the cheap cutter or sleigh with a glaring badge of cheapness as the ornament constructed from an inharmonious selection of colors and dotted to beat a Baxter St. vest lining. The dotter has no business striping or ornamenting the modern cutter or sleigh. The ornamental features of sleigh work need to be of a very high order of excellence. Otherwise it fails to correspond to the quality of finish which now obtains in all first-class establishments where sleigh work is carried on. In this connection the reader's attention is directed to examples of fine line ornaments adapted to Portland cutters and sleighs; also to examples of the bold, handsome relief scrolls once so extensively used, and which show so beautifully upon cutters and sleighs of the swell body pattern.

Ornaments Nos. 1, 2, and 3 are quick pencil sketches for panel corners. The writer contributed these pieces to *The Hub* some time ago and their reproduction must be credited to the courtesy of that journal. No. 4 is used upon the dashes of Portland cutters, speeding sleighs, etc. Two distinct corner pieces are shown in this design, thus illustrating the possibilities of variation in respect to the corner designs employed. No. 5. is a corner piece designed for Old Comfort and Empress cutters. This piece may be done in three or four shades of red, or it may be placed in gold and high lighted in relief style. In No. 6 is to be seen a very attractive design for the dash or rear panel of a large four or six passenger sleigh. No. 7 is expressly in-

FIG. 7.

tended for swell body cutters and represents an ornament familiar to many old-time painters. It is a decidedly effective scroll and will afford the student in scroll work a good working plan for further effort. Nos. 8 and 9 explain the style of the good-old fashioned scrolls which, when ably executed, may be declared the poetry of ornament. Vehicle painting lost one of its chief charms when the relief scroll was abandoned, and we say speed the day when it is welcomed back to its old time uses and prestige. Then fortunate indeed will be the painter who is able to do relief scrolling.

FIG. 8.

Transfer ornaments of the small patterns are still used and they really furnish happy little surface beautifiers at small cost. One can quickly master the work of successfully applying transfers or ''Decalcomanie,'' as our friends of the geenteel speech may say. Cut the transfer down close to its true out-lines, and then to the back of the ornament apply a size of finishing varnish and japan gold size. When this has reached the right ''tack,'' it is placed in position on the surface. It is then given a few minutes to fasten itself se-curely upon the surface, after which it is washed over with clean water until the covering over the face of the transfer is sufficiently moistened to free itself, when lo! the ornament in all its freshness and coloring of raiment is revealed. The washing of the transfer is something of a delicate operation as it is a perfectly easy matter to disfigure the ornament or flood it out of position by careless practices.

REPAINTING CUTTERS AND SLEIGHS, REVARNISHING, ETC.

Cutters and sleighs for repainting, revarnishing and brightening up generally should be got into the paint shop as soon as possible after the carriage work declines in the late fall. This enables the painter to avoid the rush which is sure to be upon him with the first"run of sleighing." It also enables him to do more satisfactory work in several ways. The work taken in early has a measure of time given it while being carried through the several processes not accorded that received late in the season. Varnish coats given proper time to dry not only surface up better but wear and retain their brilliancy longer, and do not fire crack when run out in the cold. Upon the average class of cutters and sleighs a less expensive varnish, as compared to that used upon first-class carriages, will serve all necessary purposes. Expensive finishing varnishes are not needed. Cutters and sleighs are not

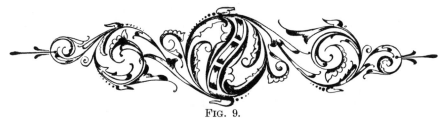

FIG. 9.

exposed to the severe and destructive forms of service that wheeled vehicles are, consequently they do not require highly elastic finishing varnishes to furnish the needed durability. They are in service for only a comparatively small part of the year, and mud spotting and troubles of that order do not intrude themselves. Save in the case of the highest-class sleigh work, a first-class gear finishing varnish will furnish satisfactory results for finishing cutter and sleigh bodies. A heavy gear varnish will answer perfectly for the running parts. But in this selection of varnishes choice should always fall upon those of first-class quality. Whatever the grade, get the best in quality of that grade. First-class paint and varnish stock is more handily worked and will cover more surface than inferior stock, and judged from any point of view one may elect it is the most economical material to buy.

When a cutter or sleigh comes in for a thorough repainting, examine the vehicle closely and if the body can be removed without too large an expenditure of labor, removal should be insisted upon. There is usually considerable dirt under the edges of a cutter body that cannot be cleaned out except the body be taken off. And a little of this dirt caught up in the paint or varnish brush worketh evil to the whole job. Moreover, the brushes brought in contact with such accumulations of dirt are unfitted to produce pleasing results in the immediate future. The touch-up-and-varnish sleigh job is, in the main, a troublesome affair, especially the running parts. The merry and pretty colors which chiefly obtain on sleigh running parts painted in former years are not so easily matched as the colors used upon the bodies. In point of fact, it doesn't pay to devote much time in trying for a match. Instead, mix a color to about the shade of the old color and go over the running parts entire. Then restripe and finish, and in the great majority of cases money will be saved thereby. In rubbing cutter or sleigh work furnished with heavy moldings out of varnish, use, for surfacing such moldings, any varnish brush of a small pattern worn to a stub. Cutting through on the edges of the moldings is nicely avoided in this way. For the large panels on sleigh work a 3-inch finishing brush will serve as the best tool. It carries a greater quantity of varnish and enables the finisher to coat the surface quicker than he could do with the smaller brush. In finishing the quick and adroit placing of the varnish is an item of chief importance.

' During the sleigh season there usually drifts into the jobbing paint shop a lot of not very particular work. As for example, heavy work, sleighs, bobs, etc. Upon such work there may be used the accumulated odds and ends of colors of various shades, hues, and tints, left over from doing sleigh work of a better class and from carriage work. Some very neat combinations may be effected by the judicious employment of these left-over bits of color, and it helps to slick up and put into profitable use certain materials which otherwise might eventually find their way into that quagmire of the paint shop—the slush keg. Briefly stated, cutter and sleigh painting opens the way for the employment of considerable material which cannot be termed strictly "available" in the other branches of painting; it comes at a time when the painter is better able to appreciate a lean loaf than a fat icicle; and if conducted according to business-like and workman-like practices it will supply a handsome source of profits.

CHAPTER XVI.

LEAVES FROM THE PAINT SHOP DIARY—PERTINENT POINTS ON PRAC-
TICAL MATTERS—BLENDING OF COLORS—SPONTANEOUS COMBUS-
TION—PAINTING IN SILVER BRONZE — THE FRENCH PAINTERS' VAR-
NISH ROOM — REMEDY FOR RUSTED CARRIAGE SPRINGS — PAINTING
METALLIC SURFACES—THINNING VARNISH—ETC.

A T best the carriage painter's existence is somewhat hazardous, his
every-day scene of toil being well laden with poisonous fumes and
fetid exhalations. In the painting of a hearse, ambulance, or ''dead
wagon'' the precaution of disinfecting the vehicle most thoroughly should
be taken. Carbolic acid, carbonate of lime, or, if one prefers, numerous
ready prepared disinfectants of penetrating composition may be used generously. Prudence dictates the policy of refusing to take any chances when
working in and about a vehicle possibly afflicted with the germs of some
deadly contagious disease.

It is not always an easy matter to clean the glasses in heavy coach work
unless special methods are practiced. Here is a quick way of cleaning be-
smeared glasses of the kind named. Saturate a soft sponge with wood alcohol and wipe over both sides of the glass. If perchance varnish or paint
accumulations are in evidence the alcohol softens them and a quick run-
around with a keen-edged putty knife removes them. If a careless or incompetent workman has badly bedaubed a glass, coat the daubs with oxalic acid.
The action of this powerful liquid will very briefly soften up the accumulations so that the putty knife will nicely slick them off. Then give a rub over
with an alcohol-charged sponge, this to be immediately followed by a smart
polish with the chamois skin. If a still better polish is desired, take a newspaper, roll it into a shape that will permit rubbing the glass without
bringing the fingers in contact with the surface, and then dipping the paper
into dry lampblack proceed to burnish both sides of the glass.

The blending of colors has lately become an important feature of the
carriage painter's art. This was at one time considered purely a matter of
business belonging to the artist, but it is not now so regarded. Artistic, and
therefore harmonious, color blending consists in preserving the individuality
of each color employed, while at the same time there is an almost unconscious
merging of one color into another. No distinctive lines are allowed to disturb the harmony of the work. The carriage color blender, like his brother
artist of the pallette and three-story studio, aims to obtain a thorough incor-

poration of all the different shades of color employed upon a certain piece of work so that the blending from light to dark may be made without resorting to any glaring contrasts.   The blending is accomplished while the colors are wet, the ground being laid first in the lighter colors, then working in the darker shades until the darkest desired shade is reached.   Great care is necessarily expended upon the tools, etc.   A color-clogged brush need not be expected to do good blending service.   No arbitrary rules can be given within which to confine the work of blending—it is too closely allied to art for that. Supremely necessary aids to success in this field of work consist of plenty of practice taken in connection with intelligent study of outline, harmony, and contrasts.

If it is desirable to varnish a job of gilding the same day the leaf is laid, and it is feared that the leaf will brush mark, it is a good plan to give the gold a light coat of thin shellac, going over the work very quickly.   The shellac will protect the leaf without in any way harming it.

One hears a good deal concerning spontaneous combustion.   The craft would be less familiar with the term if the following rule, rigidly enforced in some shops, were lived up to in letter and spirit: *Greasy rags must be burned up immediately, and not, under any consideration, allowed to remain in the shop one moment after their use is finished. Any violation of this order will result in immediate dismissal.*

The following method of filling in a badly cracked carriage surface has successfully been practiced by a friend of the writer's.   The surface is first cleaned and given a light sandpapering to strike off dirt, motes, etc.   Then dust off and apply a coat of gold-size japan, a free, generous coat of the japan being used.   Once dry, the coat is gone over with a roll of rubbing felt to kill the gloss.   The gold-size japan reaches into the minute orifices more effectively than varnish, filling and sealing the fissures, and in addition it furnishes an easily and quickly prepared surface for the color and the varnish coats to follow.

You wish to repair a split panel.   At each extremity of the split bore a ¼ inch hole.   Put one hole just at the crack, the second one fairly clear of it.   Next plug the holes up, and then dress off even with the surface of the panel.   Now cut a shallow bevel along each side of the crack; this to enable the putty to resist the cracking tendency of the crevice.   Then give the dressed off parts a coat of lead containing a good binder of oil. When this has dried putty the hollow level and fill with a putty made of ¾ dry white lead and ¼ keg lead, the liquids being rubbing varnish and japan, equal parts.   Sandpaper this repair in due time, and then give the final puttying, which should be done to the full measure of the best possible skill.

An effective little advertising card was once circulated by a keen-minded California carriage painter, and on the back of the card were appended the following wise admonitions to the carriage user.   The suggestions are quite as pertinent now as they were at the time they were first given publicity.   To

insure durability of the painting you must care for the work as follows, viz:
"Don't expose to the fumes of ammonia.
Don't let mud dry on it.
Don't scratch the varnish in washing.
Don't expose to the sun or rain when not in use.
Don't let the axle-grease collect on the hubs.
Don't blame me if you are careless, as I have given you warning."

A man is well dressed only when every part of his apparel meets the approval of the critic. This same estimate also applies to carriage painting—that is to genteel carriage painting. Hence why send the top joints on a carriage top out roughly and incompletely finished? The critical eye rests very quickly upon such conspicuous parts of a vehicle, and if they are not fittingly finished the seal of condemnation is set upon the work as a whole. Here is a finish for top joints that will disarm the fault finder: First coat up with stout coat of lead containing sufficient oil to bind the lead securely. Then mix two parts dry white lead, one part roughstuff filler, to a rather stiff paste in equal parts of japan and rubbing varnish. Rub this mixture onto the joints with a piece of heavy harness leather. When dry, give the pigment a thorough smoothing up with sandpaper, color, color-and-varnish, rub with water and pumice stone, and then finish with a hard drying finishing varnish.

To paint a carriage gear in silver bronze, which one is now and then asked to do, bring the work up to the point of the foundation color for the bronze very carefully, using no lampblack in the priming and first lead coats to throw them to a slate color. The foundation coat should be pure white, mixed to dry without gloss and applied with a camel's-hair brush. Over this coat flow on a coat of rubbing varnish, and when the right "tack" is reached apply the bronze with a soft, clean camel's-hair brush. The wiping off and the delicate burnish may be given with a soft piece of chamois skin. Stripe with some color that harmonizes nicely with the bronze, and use no varnish over it. Varnish destroys the richness of the bronze.

Why use a broad pencil in glazing double line stripes? The existing space between the stripes, when the glazing is done with a broad pencil, reflects a clouded, muddy appearance. Better glaze each line separately, using a sword pencil for glazing with, and thus obtain the best color effects along with a fine, dressy outline of striping.

If a carriage top from which the enamel has nearly or quite vanished is desired to be made bright again the following recipe, published by the writer in *Painting and Decorating* some time since, will give satisfaction: Mix 2 parts of liquid glue with 3 parts of dissolved castile soap, adding 120 parts of soft water, to more thoroughly liquify the glue and soap. Then add 4 parts of spirit varnish, after which stir in 2 parts of wheat starch, previously mixed in water. Follow with just enough lampblack to give the mixture a solidly black tinge. A trifle too much of the lampblack will kill the gloss.

The dressing is now ready for use. It should be kept in an air-tight vessel to prevent thickening.

A green stripe is strikingly enriched by glazing with verdigris, but this glaze should be varnished over as soon as dry, or, at any rate, before moisture settles upon the work; otherwise the verdigris will lose its quality.

It's a very simple operation to sweep a varnish or paint-room floor, but some ways are better than others, nevertheless. Try this way for a change and thereby establish its utility: Take a pail of sawdust, dampen it thoroughly, and then throw a windrow of the woody bits across one side of the room. Sweep across to the other side of the apartment, and then observe how spick and clean the floor will be, with no moisture remaining to annoy the painter or varnisher.

The blow-pipe should be more in evidence in the carriage paint shop. The tinsmith will charge but a small fee for making the pipe, which may be $1\frac{1}{2}$ ft. long and tapering from $\frac{1}{2}$ inch at one end to $\frac{1}{4}$ inch at the other. Dust and dirt that cannot be removed with a duster is simply given a cyclone breath through the tube, and, presto! the parts are clean. With the blow-pipe water can be driven out of evasive corners when cleaning up a job preparatory to varnishing.

Despite the best laid plans of the painter carriage linings occasionally get some glaring smears of pigment. If the linings so defaced be of light color, dampen with naphtha or gasoline, and then with a clean woolen cloth rub the goods briskly. This same treatment may be given to dark colored cloth upon which the paint spots have dried. If the spots are observed while the paint is still wet, rub them smartly with pieces of the same kind of cloth of which the lining is composed. The cloth to cloth treatment is a most effective and easy treatment.

The business wagon painter has many moldings and battens to black, and he greatly needs a good, pleasant handling pencil with which to do the work. A pretty working pencil for doing the parts here named is made in this wise: Take some hair from a camel's-hair pencil and mix with it $\frac{1}{3}$ black sable hair. Prepare a handle as though you were to make a sword pencil, splitting it at the base, etc. Then, after arranging the hair to the right width and thickness, insert the butt end of the bunch in the split. Wind tightly with strong linen thread. Use on the flat side of the pencil instead of the edge.

An imitation-of-ebony job comes within the province of the painter's skill now and then. First of all, the wood should be close, fine-grained stuff. Wash it with a decoction of logwood three or four times, allowing the liquid to dry well between applications. Next wash with a solution of acetate of iron. This gives a deep, intensely black color.

For the filling of an unusually deep surface cavity prepare a pigment after this formula: One part keg lead; 2 parts whiting. Mix to a stiff paste in equal parts of thick varnish bottoms and raw linseed oil. Add a small quantity of japan to insure reliable drying. Then to this mass mix in enough dry white lead to cause the putty to work nicely from the hand. Apply very smooth so as to avoid sandpapering.

One of the secrets of the French coach painter's success as a fine varnisher and finisher was revealed by W. H. Knight's report on the Paris Exposition. Referring to the varnish room, Mr. Knight wrote: The door is locked, and no one is admitted under any circumstances—not even the proprietor. The doors and windows are air-tight, so that not a particle of dust can find entrance. And yet the room is ventilated, but how? By means of tubes filled with a mixture of horsehair and wool. This permits the air to enter freely, but deprives it of all dust, consequently the finish of their work is perfect and exquisite.

All surfaces painted with lake colors should be amply protected by substantial varnish coats. Neither the lake coats nor the foundations over which they are laid should be allowed to dry "dead." Give the ground coats a bit of gloss and *always* use the lakes as color-and-varnish coats. Also, *always* refrain from buying a cheap, inferior lake, the chief constituents of which are whiting and aniline dye. Water dissolves the aniline; hence with water as an aid the painter can determine the quality, in a measure at least, of the lake colors. To the surface painted in a lake color, apply, before coating with varnish, a generous smear of water. If the aniline speedily disappears, leaving the colorless whiting base, the purchaser has just cause to question the quality of the material.

A varnish sag upon a surface doesn't always admit of easy removal. It can be done, however, and that very quickly and smoothly in a majority of cases. Get a stocky bunch of curled hair, wet it up thoroughly, give it a liberal dip in pulverized pumice stone, and then rub the afflicted surface carefully. Finish with a uniform polish furnished by the regular varnish surfacing equipment.

Carriage and wagon interiors, running parts, etc., finished in the natural wood, that have become stained in spots so as to be an offense to the eye, may be satisfactorily renewed by smearing the stains with oxalic acid. Apply the acid with a brush, permit it to act upon the stains for a few minutes, then with a small sponge wash off with clean, soft water. The steel scraper, handily wielded, will then remove all remaining evidences of the stains. All metallic surfaces may be perfectly cleaned with this acid.

The question of carriage springs rusting is a live one with the carriage painter. The spring maker, or rather the first-class manufacturer of springs, avers that the spring product well ground and finished is not at all liable to rust or prematurely throw off its protecting coats of paint and varnish. The carriage painter, however, is compelled to paint and dress up all sorts and conditions of springs. The badly rusted and scaly springs may be thoroughly cleaned, using a file and hammer for the purpose, and the spring layers being separated one from another. Then coat with graphite paint or mineral brown, and in due time finish up in the usual way. Again, the inner surface of the spring leaves is coated with a lead and lampblack mixture, and later given a glazing of equal parts of unsalted beef and mutton tallow. A third formula, widely known as *The Hub* formula, because it is said to have originated with that journal, has proven of value. It is as follows: "Remove the securing bolts; place the springs thus released from tension in a bath of soft water over night. In the morning, with a stiff bristle or helix brush, in water at 100° degrees, scour the plates effectually, and remove the oxide by means of an ample use of elbow grease. Dry by sunlight or artificial heat in hardwood sawdust. Let lie in warm sawdust, at 75° or 80° for from two to three hours; then give a thin coat of clear, boiled linseed oil, and when thoroughly dry (an exposure of twelve or more hours is necessary), coat over by means of a sponge with a mixture of 6 parts of commercial beeswax, suspended at 90°, with 2 parts of spirits of turpentine. One hour after application wipe off edges of all plates; then allow one hour for hardening and secure the plate with centre bolt."

The carriage painter frequently has sign writing to do on glass and he requires a reliable size to enable him to get first-class leafing. Russian isinglass makes the best size, although it is often difficult to obtain from local merchants. To a pint of soft water add a piece of the isinglass ½ in. square and boil until the material is wholly dissolved. Then add a drop or two of alcohol, strain, and the size is ready for use. Gelatine, while largely used, should be used the day it is prepared as a size, otherwise it is not reliable in its action. Put a few shreds of the gelatine in a quart of water and boil until the water is reduced to a pint.

Vermilion is one of the highly-prized carriage painting pigments, and the best is none too good to meet the requirements of good work. To test the color, heat a small quantity in a porcelain vessel over an alcohol lamp. The adulterated vermilion, in burning, will leave a sediment either red, black, or perhaps white. The genuine quicksilver vermilion invariably proves fugitive when submitted to intense heat.

The refuse oil of pine or coal tar is a useful oil to keep upon the paint shop shelves. Suppose a borrowed brush or a brush neglected in some way about the shop is found dried up—hardened to a stone-like condition. Take a quantity of the pine or coal tar oil from its air-tight receptacle, where it should be kept to prevent evaporation, and in the liquid suspend the injured brush well up over the bristles. Three or four days' immersion will usually soften up a very much abused brush.

All colors that are apparently changed in purity of color when even the palest of varnishes are used over them, should have a little of the color used in each varnish coat up to the finishing coat of varnish. If striping or ornamenting is used do this work upon the last rubbing coat and then finish with the very palest varnish obtainable.

Bear in mind this fact, namely: Colors are divided into three cardinal degrees—light, medium, and dark. And the relative position of the base color governs the intermediate shades. In the mixing and use of colors it is also a wise policy to provide for the self-asserting property of the strongest or controlling color. If this is not done the distinctive character of the color sought for will not for long be retained.

A prime factor in finishing a carriage in natural wood consists in first thoroughly cleaning the wood and then keeping it clean. All stains and discolorations of the wood should be sandpapered out or scraped off with steel scraper and a piece of glass. Then a careful, uniform sandpapering should be given. Dust off and apply a coat of raw linseed oil. This oil coat requires a clean, smooth rubbing out—as clean and smooth as a coat of paint. Give this oil coat from 24 to 36 hours to dry and harden completely. Sandpaper lightly, dust off, and give the surface a coating of some reliable, first-class, wood filler. As soon as the filler takes on a sufficient "tack," rub across the grain of the wood with soft, clean rags until the surface is free from any surplus filler. If, after the application of the filler, the cells of the wood remain unfilled or defectively sealed, a second coat of the filler will be necessary. Once the filler has dried, mix a putty colored to match the natural color of the wood, and putty nail and screw holes and other cavities. This puttying should be done so smoothly as to necessitate little or no sandpapering for the purpose of leveling the putty spots. The whole surface may now in due time be lightly gone over with No. 0 paper. Next dust off and apply a coat of pale rubbing varnish. The striping is best done on this coat. Then give second coat of rubbing, surfacing this coat, when dry, with pulverized pumice stone and water, clean up most thoroughly, and finish with a very pale durable finishing varnish.

The painting of one of these natural-wood-finished jobs often presents a formidable problem. What is the best method to pursue? That cannot be answered decisively; but a reliable method is appended. First scrape and sandpaper the old varnish clean and sleek to the wood. If the wood is in good shape and not weather-beaten, apply a coat of lead containing no more oil than is carried in the keg lead as it comes from the dealer, the pigment being simply thinned with turpentine and given a drying agent in the shape of a teaspoonful of coach japan, to, say, each pint of the mixture. If the varnish has perished, and the wood is injured thereby, it is advisable to give the lead a little extra dash of oil, but not enough to cause the lead to dry with a gloss. Testing the lead on the finger nail will determine the question of gloss. When dry this coating of lead should receive a careful sandpapering, and a second coat of lead mixed to dry "dead," and laid with a camel's-hair brush, may go on. Too much oil should be especially avoided in building the lead foundation over these natural wood surfaces, as it must be borne in mind that the grain of the wood has been already sealed with a hard, non-absorbent material into which the usual first coat percentage of oil does not penetrate. On this second coat of lead all needed puttying is done. The sandpapering which follows should be very perfect and skillfully done. Body surfaces may next receive the needed roughstuff coating up, to be subsequently rubbed out and carried through to a finish in the ordinary way. The running parts from this lead coat foundation are colored and finished according to the accepted practice.

Once upon a time, my lamented friend, A. F. Manchester, in the columns of *Varnish*, asked this pertinent question: "Do you have trouble with your fine colors clouding up and losing their brilliancy from the varnish?" Replying to the query, he suggested this plan, to the efficacy of which the writer is glad to subscribe: "On any transparent color (or any color, in fact) always add some of the color to each coat of rubbing varnish —enough to kill the amber tint of the varnish. This preserves the colors in all their original brilliancy. Of course, this plan necessitates striping and ornamenting on the last coat of rubbing, but that is just as well as burying all the tone of the colors under the varnish. Then, again, it obliges the customer to have the job revarnished when he ought."

It is not a praiseworthy practice to putty a carriage body after it is rubbed out of roughstuff, or after the first coat of color is on. The puttying should be attended to when the job is being roughstuffed—and before. All places overlooked at the first puttying should be attended to carefully upon the first coat of roughstuff. Puttying upon a roughstuffed rubbed panel leads to premature surface blemishes of a most unhappy order.

Certain of the yellows are rather difficult to work nicely when used as striping colors for dagger or sword pencils. Notably so is chrome yellow, which, by the way, is a pretty foundation for glazing with carmine. Such colors may be remedied by adding a bit of some body color which will give them a stronger covering property without harmfully changing the purity of the yellow.

The subject of varnish rooms is an entertaining one. So many poor varnish rooms exist that any plan to make them better, so long as it be a feasible plan, merits attention. Mr. F. J. Flowers, an old-time carriage man and an earnest advocate of the first-class varnish room, some time ago gave his idea of such an apartment in these words: "First, it should not be on the top floor of a building where it gets all the gases and fumes from the smith and paint shops. It should be round in form, with a dome roof, ventilated and well lighted therefrom; and each light of glass should be as colorless as possible, and arranged so as to prevent the direct rays of the sun. Its ceiling should be all wood, stained light blue with water colors; the floor should be waxed or oiled; the room, when in use, should be kept at an even temperature (not less than 65°), and all dampness should be avoided. You ask, why round? I answer, all evaporations form in circles when ascending; the room having no corners, there is no back draught to obstruct them. Why lighted from the roof? There will be no cross-lights, hence no conflicting light. Why ceiled with wood? It is dryer than plaster and will absorb the evaporations when not coated with oil paint. Why color blue? It is the spring light, and gives the purest reflection. Why an even temperature? It will prevent the condensing of the vapor, and thereby prevent it from falling back upon the varnish, which gives it that bloomy, silky, and pitted look which we hear so much about.''

Upon heavy vehicle work, such as broughams, landaus, etc., the inside surface of glass frames, pillars, door checks, and the like, quite commonly go with a polish finish, as it does away with sticking doors, defaced pillars, and glaring glass frames. The contrast between the polished parts and those reflecting a high brilliancy of finish is soft and pleasing and a grateful relief to the eye. The parts referred to, having been brought up to a solid foundation of rubbing varnish, are given a thorough surfacing with pumice stone flour and water. Next rub with sweet oil and rotten stone, using a soft woolen cloth for the polisher. Conclude the operation by rubbing wheat flour under a clean bit of woolen until the friction generated makes a gloss. The flour, in addition to its other office, will absorb and clean up the oil.

A very quick drying striping color is frequently demanded—one that can be varnished over in an hour after application, or sooner. Mix the pigment in equal parts of rubbing varnish and coach japan. Then thin to the proper working consistency with turpentine.

In painting over metallic surfaces, which the carriage and wagon painter frequently finds it necessary to do, it is essential to first know that such surfaces are thoroughly clean and free from acids, grease, etc. Give them a rub over with kerosene or benzine, and then wash with soap and water, concluding with a generous rinsing off with clean water. If the surface is too heavily saturated with paint injuring accumulations, give it a wash with water containing sal soda in the proportion of, say, $\frac{1}{2}$ to $\frac{3}{4}$ lb. of the soda to 5 or 6 quarts of water. A rinsing with clean water will now afford a clean surface over which to paint. The metallic surface being clean, it remains for the painter to give it a hard, solid surfacing with No. $1\frac{1}{2}$ sandpaper, in order to develop the necessary minute furrows and scratches to give the pigment a ''bite'' or a chance to grip fast. Instead of sandpapering, the practice holds good in some shops of rubbing the surface with a fire brick as a means of trenching and channeling it to the required extent.

The vehicle painter located in the small shop and not usually using a very considerable quantity of varnish daily, should buy his supply of this material in small cans—pints and quarts for example. Once a can is opened, the varnish, through repeated exposure to the air, quickly begins to grow fatty, and after a time the loss of the turpentine leaves it in an unfit condition to work satisfactorily over a fine surface. A rubber stopper is the best kind of a varnish can stopper, because it does not crumble and break into bits like the cork, and it is the closest possible approach to an air-tight device.

The painter has but small use for the varnish that has to be thinned with turpentine in order to give it the proper spreading and flowing property. The elements of durability and brillancy of lustre are in great danger of being greatly impaired, if not quite wholly destroyed, when shop thinning of varnishes is practiced. To attempt to successfully cut the solidity of varnish with turpentine added in hit or miss fashion constitutes a direct injury to this manifestly sensitive and delicate material. Thinning varnish should be resorted to only when an extremely critical emergency presents itself.

To provide a tight, dust-and-smoke-proof floor for the varnish room, proceed in this wise: Cut strips of stout wrapping paper to the proper length to fit lengthwise of the floor. Coat one side of the paper with trimmer's paste, and then lay the strips on smooth and free from wrinkles. Allow the second strip to overlap the first one fully 2 inches. Continue overlapping until the floor is covered. When the first layer or covering has laid long enough to provide for the complete drying of the paste, lay a second course of the paper in the same manner, and in due time, if necessary, apply a third course. Then apply a coat of yellow ochre paint, mixed oil and turpentine, in the proportion of $\frac{1}{4}$ oil to $\frac{3}{4}$ turpentine, with a tablespoonful of japan added to each pint of the paint. The second coat of ochre may be mixed in $\frac{2}{3}$ hard drying implement varnish to $\frac{1}{3}$ japan.

Mr. P. C. Hoebel, in *Varnish*, interestingly decribes his method of painting over a cracked and fissured surface, and avers that it has for many years proven uniformly successful. Mr. Hoebel says: "Instead of sanding down the old varnish, I skin it off by the use of ammonia and a stiff bladed putty knife. Then rub down with block rubbing stone and let stand over night to dry out. Next, a good sandpapering with No. 1 paper; dust thoroughly. Then apply a mixture composed of 1 part drop black, 1 part keg lead, and the same amount of dry lampblack. Add a little rubbing varnish. Thin to a proper working consistency with turpentine. Next day putty-glaze the entire cracked surface with not too soft putty. Use the regulation hard drying carriage painter's putty. This putty should dry hard enough to sand well the following day. The sandpapering of this putty is of the greatest importance and requires an extra amount of elbow grease. The job is now ready to receive the proper ground work for its respective color which is to be."

In wagon painting some exceedingly light and delicate tints are used, and driers for such tints adapted to the delicacy of coloring are needed. Appended is a formula for a drier of this kind: Mix 15 parts of sulphate of zinc, 4 parts sugar of lead, and 7 of litharge, with pure linseed oil, and grind the mixture in a paint mill very fine; then mix 100 parts of paris white to a dough with 50 parts of white lead and linseed oil. Grind this also very fine in the mill, then mix all together, grinding once more.

It is possible now and then to remedy a case of pitted varnish in this manner. The morning after the varnish is applied cover the surface with clear turpentine. Let the turps gradually soak up and soften the pitted

varnish, adding more turps as required. When the varnish has become sufficiently softened, mix a little raw linseed oil with the turpentine (the oil
holding the turps in check and preventing it from cutting into the under
coats) and with a soft badger-hair brush proceed to "lift" the afflicted varnish
coat. The varnish once removed, let the surface stand for a few hours,
then give it a light rubbing over with a moistened sponge dipped in finely
pulverized pumice stone. Follow with a thorough washing with clean water
and revarnish.

Color and varnish strainers are a necessity. Cheese cloth, cut into 6-
inch squares, gives a very practical kind of strainer. All colors that have
stood for some time after mixing require straining before being used. And
finishing varnish—all varnish, in fact, should be strained as the final contents of the can are approached. Many first-class finishers insist upon
straining all the varnish they use; and cheese cloth serves the purpose of a
good strainer at a low cost.

The best stroke for squaring up varnish has often been discussed at
length, and it seems to be the decision of the leading finishers of the country that the horizontal stroke is to be preferred to the vertical. To the beginner the former is probably the most difficult to use, the danger of runs,
sags, etc., seemingly being thereby intensified. The natural flow of varnish,
as the finishers all may know, is downward, and the horizontal stroke of the
brush does not arrest this flow or divert it from its accepted course. The
vertical stroke, however, permits of a varnish flow in at least two directions
—sideways and downward. Runs and other surface defacers are equally
possible with the horizontal or vertical brush stroke. Immunity from such
disturbers depends altogether upon the uniformity and equality with which
the varnish has been flowed upon the surface.

To renovate and give a fresh new look to cushions and backs, when
faded, thin the desired color down with turpentine until it can almost be
called a wash, and apply the mixture very thinly. Allow the color to dry
thoroughly, and then thin shellac with alcohol until a very thin shellac is
provided and coat the articles with this, following immediately with a smart
polishing with neatsfoot oil and then wiping dry with clean woolen cloths.

The twine used for bridling paint brushes—and the twine bridle is the
favored kind in the carriage paint shop—should be run through melted tallow and beeswax before put to use. After the tallow and wax has cooled on
the twine, the bridling may proceed. After the twine is in position on the
brush, run a little of the warm grease and wax over it. Thus a more durable
and more easily cleaned bridle is given the brush.

Imitation vermilions are considerably favored of late years, but they
fade after the manner of a late autumn twilight unless amply protected by
varnish. Given adequate varnish protection they show radiant colors and
wear durably.

The country carriage painter is no stranger to the vehicle, the family heirloom, perchance, that comes into the shop with hubs split and shattered, and axle grease filtering up through the cracks saturating the wood and making it generally unpaintable. An old carriage painter advises this treatment in order to cause the paint and color to dry over the afflicted parts: First give the hubs a wash with gasoline or benzine, working the fluid well into the cracks. Give plenty of time for evaporation to occur. Then with shellac cut with a little ether, fill in the fissure. Next make a putty of plaster of paris mixed with the shellac and ether. Into the fissures force this mixture, keeping it clearly from the outside surface of the hub, as nothing short of a file will level it after it has dried. Give the putty a nice, smooth dressing off upon the filling of each crevice.

The business wagon occasionally contains a window glass that should go in imitation of frosted glass. Take finely ground whiting and, with $\frac{2}{3}$ raw linseed oil to $\frac{1}{3}$ japan, mix to a rather stiff consistency; and then with turpentine reduce to a condition to work easily under a camel's-hair brush. Let the mixture be spread quickly and uniformly even upon the glass. Then take finely shredded cloth and roll it into a ball and cover with a clean cotton cloth and proceed to go carefully over the freshly laid on whiting, softly tapping it, until the frosted imitation is brought clearly and prettily into relief.

A surface that has become dented by a blow from a hammer or other blunt instrument can be remedied by so placing the surface that the dent or depression will hold a little water poured into it, and then holding a lighted taper to the water until the heat thus generated in the minute body of water causes the wood to again assume its natural shape and condition. In denting the wood, if a positive rupture does not occur at the edge of the depression the strain of the wood has occured in two distinct directions—inward and lengthwise—and the reaction when it takes place will be two-fold. A second way of treating such surface difficulties consists of boring with a gimlet through the compressed fibres of the wood until the sound timber is reached. This puncture will counteract the lengthwise reaction. Then moisten with tepid water until the wood recovers its natural position again. The bruise or dent with fractured edges is more easily repaired, as no reaction need be feared, the pressure of the tool making the depression having overcome the natural resistance of the wood; and destruction of resistance results, as may be naturally inferred, in destruction of all reactive functions.

If the carriage or wagon painter at any time wishes a varnish to dry without gloss he may dissolve 4 ounces of beeswax in turpentine and add to 1 quart of varnish. This, while not reducing the body of the varnish, will cause it to dry without much, if any, lustre. It will work from the brush freely and wear durably. If only a subdued gloss is desired, use 2 ounces of beeswax to 1 quart of varnish.

The window sashes in business wagons that are painted in some of the dark fashionable greens offer a beautiful contrast to the body color if grained mahogany color. For the ground color for the mahogany use white lead, burnt sienna, and a bit of raw sienna for the toning ingredient. Putty, if necessary, upon the first ground coat. Two coats should suffice to give a dense, stable ground. Burnt sienna, wet in stale beer, forms the graining material. Apply with a soft brush, wipe quickly out with a soft, fleecy sponge, use the blender lightly, and the trick is done.

The finisher should never assume the responsibility of adding driers to varnish. Varnish is composed of peculiarly sensitive and susceptible ingredients responding to the slightest influences, good or ill, and the addition of siccatives only tends to make the action of the varnish uncertain. It is only for the time being that the driers unite and form a part of the varnish. During the operation of applying to the surface the varnish forsakes or separates the shop-added siccative, with the result that pitting and pin-holing, along with other burdensome deviltries, are developed. No, shop mixing of driers with varnish is not advisable.

My esteemed *confrere*, Mr. J. G. Cameron, makes public this worthy observation, with *Varnish* as his medium of circulation: "Every varnish room should have a window through which the direct rays of the sun passes dur-the afternoon. It should be curtained and have a small slit or hole in the curtain for a slice of sunlight to stream through. This slice of sunlight will reveal the condition of the air within the room and tell the varnisher just how must dust he will have to contend with that day. If this ray shows that the air is loaded with magnetic dust, it would be well for him to sprinkle well every suspicious place within the varnish room. Some days sprinkling is not needed; such days as rainy ones or right after a rain•storm. On windy days, window sills and any place where the air is likely to drift through should be wet down. But on magnetic days the floor and every place should be well wet down. A varnisher's clothes should be also scrupulously groomed off. The writer has varnished often with a damp 'shammy' wrapped round his wrist and arm to keep the dust from his underclothing from troubling him."

Beware of the black color-and-varnish that carries a dash of too much color in it. Black of high or low degree, such as is-used in carriage painting, may be classed as a non-drying material. Finishing varnish applied over a color-and-varnish containing too great a percentage of color is exceedingly liable to strike into this improperly hardened undercoat and lose the beauty of its lustre thereby. In carriage part finishing done upon the color-and-varnish coat the trouble here noted should be guarded against.

Ornamental striping upon business wagons should never be done with the heavy stripe. Retain the same style of striping throughout a job. Throwing in two or three styles of line work on a job is an affront to good taste of which no up-to-date painter should be guilty.

A fine old woodworker once told my lamented friend, Mr. C. E. Vader, how to make a saw with which to cut block pumice stone. He said:"Take a piece of band iron 1¼ or 2 inches wide and 18 inches long; put one end in the vise and then get a sharp cold-chisel. Be sure to have it sharp. Slant the chisel 45° from you and tip to the left and strike quite a blow. Next time turn chisel to the right, or just try to cut some saw teeth in this iron. You can cut and set them at the same time. Don't make teeth too far apart. This will cut as much pumice stone as a well filed and set saw would."

In an essay on "How to Make Coach Varnish go Wrong," published by a prominently-known varnish making firm some time since, this advice was tendered: "Practice hospitality! Let everybody go in and out of your varnish room freely. Don't have a small door cut in the large one, and don't shut off your varnish room from the other rooms. Let the temperature of your varnish room vary as much as possible. Under no circumstances allow it to remain the same for two consecutive hours. Let it fall far below 70° or rise far above 80°; but above all things, *make it vary*. In the winter season let the fire go out occasionally, and be sure to select this as the proper time to open the window to see what is going on outside."

One of the strong selling factors of a vehicle consists of a first-class interior finish. A prospective customer, as a rule, is quick to perceive the finish of the inside surface; and nothing tends more powerfully to cheapen the looks of an otherwise faultlessly finished job than a slovenly surfaced and finished carriage body interior. One doesn't need to insist upon the same high standard of cleanliness for the inside as the outside, but good surfacing and an excellent freedom from dirt, motes, etc., should be maintained in the finishing of interior surfaces.

In the finishing of carriages in the natural wood, gum shellac should not be used to fill up the grain of the wood. Shellac is of an entirely too brittle nature, devoid of elasticity, to be used upon a surface subject to sustained vibrations with accompanying violent jars and jolts. For first-class carriage work shellac is good only when not used.

Another strongly recommended method of filling up cracks and fissures in coach panels embraces the employment of equal parts of English filling, dry white lead and whiting, mixed with equal parts of japan and rubbing varnish. To this add ½ the quantity of rye flour paste, stirring the mass into a thick consistency. This is applied with an old paint brush, and when it has set and stiffened considerably upon the surface it is knifed in with a broad-blade putty knife, and two days later it is rubbed down with a block of pumice stone or a fine rubbing brick.

A putty for resetting glass in coach frames is made of 7 parts whiting and 1 part white lead mixed to the correct working consistency in raw linseed oil, adding a little japan gold size to furnish the proper drying quality. If the putty is to be use upon black frames, darken sufficiently with ivory drop black, instead of lampblack, and lessen proportionately the japan used. This putty can be depended upon to remain in place and securely hold the glass in the frames.